Struggles of a

Dreamer

The Battle Between a
Dream and Tradition

Yahaya Baruwa

Praise for Yahaya Baruwa and *Struggles of a Dreamer*

"Yahaya describes the bitter-sweet reality of one's journey in life in a meaningful way. He gets across a strong message in his book regarding hope, which is much needed in life itself and our community today."

Jamna Kaur, author of *Disciples Journey*

"When I reflect on *"Struggles of a dreamer"* with the beggar on the New York City streets, I realize that we have to be thankful of our lives and take advantage of the opportunities that are around us. I'm a firm believer in the saying that everything happens for a reason and this coincides with the quote stated in the chapter, "When the worst happens to you in life, it is not life punishing you: its life pushing you to wake up" I feel as if that's the reason why we should prevail in every situation. As I read this chapter I realize that every dream or goal doesn't come easy; there's a struggle. And along with this struggle comes determination as to which the beggar was determined to rise above his misfortune and determined to seek gratification. With that being said I learn to endure my struggles and to remain determined. *Struggles of a Dreamer.*"

With Courtesy,
Tyrone "Yung Spot" Taiwo

"I like the part about having vision and faith in one's dream. These two qualities helped me become a millionaire! I believe they can help you realize your dreams, too."

David "Super Dave" Ogunnaike, author of *The Millionaire Genius: How to Wake Up the Money Magic within You*

"Yahaya Baruwa depicts the labyrinth of life and the value of simple wisdom at our finger tips, worth a consideration. A must read book to unlocking your special dream."

Isaac Nii Akrong MA, PhD Cand. York University
Founder: African Dance Ensemble (ADE)
www.afridance.com

"A dream is an imaginative picture in the mind of the dreamer. But only struggle and hard work makes a scene in reality."

-Musty Marshal

"*Struggles of a Dreamer* is a valuable read from a super-optimist to the completely cynical. This book taught me that no matter how down you are with life, you will always be given an opportunity to find balance. Knowledge and courage are the keys to seeing and acting on the opportunity."

Enan Hoque

"A surprisingly tender book—it makes a powerful point about what can happen to a man caught between his dreams and tradition. What can he possibly do to succeed? Join the dreamer in his struggle!"

Maria Viloria

"No dream comes through without adversity and hurdles. As a Canadian citizen for about five years, and now a recent graduate in human resource management, I can definitely relate, When you read the book *Struggles of a Dreamer: The Battle between a Dream and Tradition*, you will definitely be reassured that the sky is the limit, especially when you feel stuck in a situation where can't get out."

Rhonda Victor

"A powerful and inspiring tale that takes place in a land where the only limit to one's success is the value one puts on their potential. This is a moving tale that builds a relationship with the reader as we follow Tunde's struggle, when he has nothing but his motivated spirit."

Ajeet Sidhu

"Winning doesn't always mean being first, winning means you are doing better than you've done before. I am inspired. Great job, Yahaya!"

Kunle "K-Money" Adekale, President, Stash-House Entertainment

"'Often when the worst happens to you in life, it is not life punishing you; it is life pushing you to wake up.' *Struggles of a Dreamer: The Battle between a Dream and Tradition* is an inspirational book filled with powerful and moving life lessons! Reading this book will give you the courage to move forward in life and to get back on the right foot. Overall, a great read!"

Timothy Chiu, University Student

"We all dream. Every once in a while we have the audacity to pursue these dreams. This book serves to remind us of the powerful potential that lies dormant within our deepest aspirations."

Michael MacDonald, Toronto, Ontario

"I was very intrigued and motivated by your approach to life, and it has given me a somewhat different perspective on life. You're a very inspirational person."

Mohamed Hussein

"The body is like an engine, and faith mixed with persistence is the gasoline. Read this book over and over again; it is a constant supply of the gasoline you need to keep going."

Kelechi Amadi, Real Estate Sales Representative, Century 21

"Having a dream is one thing, and acting on that dream is another. Read *Struggles of a Dreamer* if you are between the two; it may give you that kick you need to start acting on your dream!"

Pauline Rankin, Acclaimed Speaker and Personal Development Coach

"Every dream comes with its unique struggles; only determination can take you to your dreamland. Four years in the youth office, I had dreams, and I had to struggle to accomplish them. *Struggles of a Dreamer* is a must-read. This life-changing book inspired me to continue to pursue my goals."

Comrade Samuel Umachi, Youth President, the Presbyterian Church of Nigeria

"We all strive to find our purpose in life. This book captures that light-bulb moment of change. A beauty of a tribute to life's evolution."

Femi Doyle-Marshall, Fitness Professional, Entrepreneur

"As a student and foreign born, I could relate to *Struggles of a Dreamer*. The story motivated and encouraged me not to give up easily when I face obstacles in life. Like the character Tunde, we should instead look ahead positively with hope for a good future as we go through life. I will recommend this book to others, because it teaches us how we can go from zero to hero.

Khadija Othman

Struggles of a Dreamer

The Battle Between a Dream and Tradition

Yahaya Baruwa

Tapestry House Publishing

Library and Archives Canada Cataloguing in Publication

Baruwa, Yahaya
Struggles of a dreamer : the battle between a dreamer
and tradition / Yahaya Baruwa.

ISBN 978-0-9866991-0-8

I. Title.

PS8603.A787S87 2010   C813'.6   C2010-905247-1

Edited by Andrea Lemieux
Design and layout by AtriTeX Technologies P Ltd
Cover design by Sheraz Maqsood, gillanesolutions.com
Author photograph by Michael McIntosh

Tapestry House Publishing

Yahaya Baruwa
388 King Street West
PO Box 30035 King St PO
Toronto, Ontario
M5V 0A3

www.strugglesofadreamer.com

Printed and bound in Canada

Struggles of a Dreamer

Acknowledgments

To my sweet parents, Hajia and Maroof Baruwa. Never could I repay you for your sacrifices and patience or the effort you make for my siblings and me. I still do not know how you do it. With my whole heart, thank you. I love you both.

To my sister, Rasheedat, and brothers, Suleman, Habib, Usman, Azeez, Abubakar and Mohammed. Without you, I would be lost, but, fortunately, you were always there when I needed you most. Thank you!

To my friend, Joy Edward. You were the light at the end of the dark tunnel when the going got hard. Your enthusiasm and kind, cheerful words never seemed to run out. Much love and gratitude to you.

To my mentors, who have spent countless hours sharing with me their knowledge and experience. Maxim Weithers, David Ogunnaike, Dr. Isa Odidi, George Philipou, Bradley Sugars, Alhaji Tajudeen, Bob Proctor, Pauline Rankin, Andre Abrigo, Gerry Roberts, David Flynn, Heidy Lawrance, and others, I thank you all.

And to all the dreamers in the struggle, keep going no matter what, for you will never know how close you were to making your dream a reality if you give up.

The individuals who made this book possible:

Aisha and Salma Abdulhamid
Alexandria Williams
Ali Arshad
Andrew Lee
Chinedu Mgadi
Khadijat and Taofik Baruwa
Fernando Bonjov
Brenda and Friends at Brenda's Family Restaurant
Mary Coggan
Habib Olawale
Hajia and Maroof Baruwa
Super Dave and Family
Maria Delapane
Melissa Dore
Reyna Dy
Joy Edward
Dr. Dan Farine
Mustapha "Musty" Marshal
Nicholson Farray
Nigerian Student Association at York University
Jennifer Fletcher
Josephine Maryo
Dr. H. Keunen
Dr. C. Maxwell
Dr. Isa and Dr. Amina Odidi
Karen Muller

Paolo Ortega
Violet Phillips
Megan Prosper
Abubakar Sadiq
Janel Slater
Myla Tan
Maxim Weithers
York University Black Student Association

The author would like to seize the opportunity to show gratitude to the above individuals and all others for their financial support and countless hours they contributed toward the successful completion of this book.
Thank you!

Preface

They say that the best way to learn something and truly internalize it is to teach others the knowledge you are trying to make your own. This is one of many reasons why I decided to put pen to paper and begin to write this book.

As a young businessman, I have found that, like all of us, I have certain strengths and many weaknesses. My aim in writing this book was to strengthen my weaknesses by sharing with you the knowledge I have acquired through study and by talking with many successful men and women from all walks of life, so that you can also become inspired to better your own life and the lives of those around you.

The process was not as easy or straightforward as I had anticipated. In fact, it was quite difficult. Apart from having a hard time deciding what my book was going to be about and how I was to write it, it took me over a year of persistence, many sleepless nights at my parents' dining table on my ancient laptop computer, and long hours of dreaming, while at the same time trying to overcome the stress caused by the fear of failure.

Even though I didn't know where to start, I knew that I did not want my book to be just like all the other books on the shelves that analyze your habits, and then try to build you up, brick by brick, in a slow and boring process. Please do not misunderstand me, there is nothing wrong with those books. In fact, some of them helped me transform into a better individual. I just wanted my book to be different.

So I chose the path less traveled. I wrote this book as much for your entertainment as for inspiration. Why? Because I believe that we are more open to learning when what we are reading is interesting—like a really good story. *Struggles of a Dreamer* will delight you, make you laugh, bring tears to your eyes, frighten you, hold you in suspense, and be a romantic experience. With this plan, how could I go wrong, because there is bound to be something in it for everyone?

Little did I expect to experience some life-altering changes during the writing of this book. In particular, I gained an understanding of my relationship with my parents, especially my father.

Frankly, I have to admit that I had a very rigid relationship with my father. I thought that he was the last person on earth who would fully support my ambition to become a successful businessman. As fate would have it, I became stuck and didn't know how to conclude the book, and as I began to seek the best ending for it, with the guidance of my mentors, I realized that my father was as innocent and kind as anybody else's father. His constant urging to pursue a safer and more secure career path was not because he was ignorant about what I wanted; but because he cared for his children and wanted them to stand among great people, people who are not dependent on anyone but themselves. He just did not want to see us fail.

I no longer see my father in a negative light. I now understand that his motives are to protect his loved ones. And with this in mind, I am able to put more effort toward my dreams without any feelings of guilt or disappointment. After all, we both have the same goal.

Thus, it is with great joy that I present to you *Struggles of a Dreamer: The Battle between a Dream and Tradition.* I hope that you will enjoy reading it just as much as I have enjoyed writing it.

To your success,
Yahaya Olanrewaju Baruwa

Part One

Picking up the scraps on the streets of New York City

It was hot and humid on another busy day in New York City. People, the young and the old, rushed up and down the sidewalks, and hundreds of yellow cabs filled the streets, honking impatiently for the cars in front to move forward so they could deliver their passengers to their destinations and pick up their next fare, all with the purpose of making a decent profit before the end of their shift.

In the midst of all this activity, shadowed by such grandeur as the Trump Tower; the Empire State Building; and high-class corporate buildings, condos, hotels, and shops, sat a quiet, homeless beggar of about twenty-seven years of age.

The expression on his face was unmistakably one of misery and unhappiness. His face was dirty, and his overgrown hair, although black, was now a brownish color, emphasizing its need for clean, warm water and a shampoo.

His only possessions were a tattered brown knitted sweater that he wore with a pair of black pants, a metal bowl that was bent out of shape and served as a container for a hot meal and to collect change from the generous passersby, a worn-out rug that he sat on, a ragged sleeping bag, and an old pillow on which to lay his head at night.

Fortunately for him, the streets of New York were populated with many well-to-do men and women, thus the greater were his chances of getting enough coins to buy his next meal. So as not to miss every opportunity to collect a coin, the beggar would sit on the sidewalk day after day, night after night, to the point where many of the people who worked in the nearby office buildings would look out for him after their lunch break to give him their leftover change.

One afternoon, a few hours before rush hour, a dark-green Bentley Continental GT pulled up to the curb in front of the spot the man had chosen to sit for the past many months. The car gleamed under the sun. The young beggar had seen many like it, and this one did not excite him, "After all," he thought to himself, "a person that rich has no time for a man as poor as I am."

Then a strange thing happened. The car's four-way flashers came on and the driver stepped out without switching off the car. This puzzled the beggar. "This person must have stopped because of me; after all, the closest store is down the street, and there are parking spaces available there," he thought.

The beggar felt intimidated as the figure seemed to be heading toward him. She was a young African-American woman who appeared to be a business executive. Shy and ashamed, the beggar bowed his head, looking into his metal bowl, which held a five dollar bill and five quarters.

The woman did not say a word, she only handed to him a large brown envelope with nothing written on it. He looked up and she smiled at him as he accepted her mysterious gift. She then departed in the magnificent piece of machinery, the smooth engine humming a pleasing song as it vanished into the busy streets of the city.

Excited about his good fortune, the man quickly hid the envelope beneath his sweater and went to look for a deserted place, away from the watchful eyes of anyone who might want a part, or worse, all, of the treasure he was sure was contained in the envelope. In his excitement, he did not bother to take his possessions with him as he ran across the busy street and made his way to the back of a small, low-rise building.

"God damn you!" the beggar exclaimed suddenly in disappointment as he took a peek inside the envelope. He had expected to see a bundle of cash, but instead he realized that he had been the victim of a cruel joke. "The stupid, cheapskate lady with her flashy car just needed some amusement in her boring day, and I, a poor innocent man, am her entertainment!" he thought angrily.

The envelope contained a book and nothing else, not even a quarter. Angry, and without examining the book, the beggar dropped it back into the envelope and threw it against the wall with all the power he could summon, leaving it where it landed in a corner between two walls.

Disappointed, the beggar walked slowly back to his accustomed begging spot, kicking out of his path the garbage that lay on the ground and thinking, "Without a doubt I am a fool to actually have believed that a poor beggar like me could expect even as little as a dime from such a rich person. Who was I kidding?" Realizing that the end of the work day was near, he began to pick up his pace, as this was the time of day that promised more than he could ever hope to get from some woman in a Bentley, or any other such person for that matter.

"Hey! Hey! Hey! What the hell are you doing?" the beggar screamed at two men who were taking away his possessions. A storekeeper stood nearby overseeing the operation as the two men carelessly tossed the beggar's rug, sleeping bag, metal bowl, and other possessions into the back of a black pickup truck. "Where are you taking my things? This is all I've got!" he cried out, running to catch the two men before they got into the truck and sped away, but he was too late.

Upset, first about the cruel joke played on him by the rich woman, then about the two men who had taken his things, he went over to the storekeeper. "This was the only solution to your stubbornness," the storekeeper began. "I have asked you kindly many times to pack up and leave my storefront, but you would not listen, that is why I called the trash collectors, paying with money out of my own pocket, to take your junk away. It is going to a place more worthy of your kind. After all, such a filthy man as you does not belong in such prestigious city streets as these." All this the storekeeper said in a hurtful and arrogant tone to condemn the poor beggar.

Feeling powerless, the beggar could not summon the will to fight back; after all, an empty, growling stomach and an unhappy soul are no match for a well-fed, healthy, proud, and arrogant man. Instead, with his head bowed, the beggar turned away and began to walk in the direction the truck had taken with his only possessions, while the storekeeper stood laughing and rejoicing at his unjust victory.

Many days had turned into months since his possessions were taken away by the two trash collectors. The beggar's stomach complained more angrily and loudly as each day passed. Failing to find his things after much searching, he decided it best to start all over again, only this time he had to be content with a side street. Only a few people came by each day, even rush hour did not offer much action.

Unlike the last street he was on, on this street he got less than twenty bucks each day instead of the forty to sixty, or even as much as one hundred dollars that he got on some days.

Often the worst things that happen to us are a slap on the face, awakening us to the reality of what has become of our life, each and every time leaving us with the choice to either mend the past and redirect our path to a more favorable one, or to continue down the same path, destined to be led by the random wind, whose destination is never predictable. Just this, the beggar was about to realize.

The blinding glare of the florescent lighting in the emergency room forced the beggar to close his eyes after his first attempt to open them. "Where am I," he asked of a young lady in white who stood over him.

"You are in the emergency room of the hospital," she replied with a comforting smile. "Do you not remember what happened to you last night?" The beggar had no answer and only looked confused. The nurse continued, "You must count yourself a very, very lucky man. You were attacked and beaten almost to death, but fortunately, a man who was passing by the alley where you lay unconscious called an ambulance, and out of the goodness of his heart, he even paid for the extensive treatment needed to patch you up, knowing that a beggar would not be able to afford the high medical fee. I doubt that you recall him, but he said he sees you begging on the sidewalk on his way to and from work."

The beggar was embarrassed. Without a word, he looked away from the nurse, and turning his face the other way, he saw his reflection in the large window that overlooked the city lights and tears began to roll down his cheeks. "What has become of the son of my father? My life? Have I really lost hope in living? What happened to the life I once lived? My good family? My job? My dignity and respect?" Questions such as these flooded the mind of the beggar. "Here I am, a beggar, once at the brink of death, yet I have been given another chance. I could continue to be a beggar, relying for my existence on the undependable and untrustworthy hands of my fellow men and women and die an undignified death, leaving nothing worthwhile to be remembered by, or I could seize the opportunity of this second chance and live a more dignified and respected life."

As if a switch had been turned from off to on, the beggar in an instant came alive once again. He sat up in his bed, struggling because of the sharp pains in his stomach and wounds on his face and arms, but with a smile on his face.

"You must watch yourself!" exclaimed the nurse in a caring tone as she moved to help him. "Your injuries are not even a day old; you must be careful not to make them worse."

The beggar smiled, indifferent to the pain, "I apologize," he said, "it isn't in my nature to not introduce myself, especially to one as caring and kind as you." The man introduced himself as Tunde, pronouncing his name in his strong Nigerian accent, emphasizing the two syllables equally.

"My name is Jane," said the nurse shyly. She continued cautiously, "Tell me Tunde, how is it that a gentleman such as you lives in a manner that a less competent man would not choose to live?"

"I am quite surprised that you have asked me such a question. Nobody in all my time as a beggar on the streets of New York has ever cared to ask me that. Nobody ever cared to know how things could come to such a pass for a perfectly able man."

"My story is one full more of sorrow than of happiness. When I was young and had recently graduated with a degree as a chartered accountant from the University of Lagos, popularly known as UNILAG, my wife and I decided to get married. We had been a couple for over four years, and both our cultures looked down on intimate relationships between unmarried couples."

"After many years of struggling without much success to get a job as an accountant, I decided it would be best if I settled for any job I could find to make ends meet. My wife had been fortunate enough to get a job in her field as a teacher at a polytechnics college, but as time went by, she and I began to grow further apart. Not because we no longer loved each other, but because I had to pound the hot pavement day and night in other towns looking for a job to support our family, which was about to grow, as our first child was on the way. We could not count on anyone else; each family member had to work in order to survive, and the many things we would need for our growing family were rising in price."

"One day," said Tunde enthusiastically, "I had the good fortune of getting a job with a rich man who lived about a day's journey from my city. It was a short-term contract as a security guard at his very large house," he said, gesturing with wide-open arms to emphasize the size of the house. "Back home a security guard was known as a gateman. My job was to greet and take care of the needs of each visitor to the house, and to open the gate in a timely manner when my boss arrived in his big SUV."

"Did you not mind being a security guard after all those years of hard work to get your university degree?" asked the nurse in sympathy. "I mean, I spent only a few years in college studying to become a nurse, and it was not the easiest of tasks."

"Yes, it was very difficult. Each and every night I laid my head to sleep in the small cramped shed that I called my home. It hurt me to think of what had become of the son of my father, and what I had to settle for. And on top of this, the thought of my wife, lonely in the dark apartment that rarely enjoyed the beauty of its walls in the evening because of the never-ending power failures that made already miserable lives even more miserable. It was like adding hot pepper to a freshly made wound, a wound that would remain as fresh as it was when it first happened."

Tears rolled down Tunde's cheeks. But because of his pride, he quickly wiped them away and acted as if nothing had happened. The nurse noticed, however, and wanted to hug him, but she didn't, thinking that it would be in vain.

"Every day I thought about how much better life would be when I would be able to care for my wife and our little boy, who was already starting to take his first steps on his own. I didn't give up hope, though; I thought that as long as there was a God up there, this misfortune would one day be history."

"Then one late evening when I thought things could not possibly get any worse, there was a loud banging at the giant black and gold gate that intersected the high walls that surrounded my boss's home and that provided an entrance to the large compound. I heard the innocent voice of a young woman, and that is what I saw when I peered through the peeping slot. She said she was my boss's sister-in-law and that she had come from the village. Without any further thought, I proceeded to open the gate, after all, this was not the first, second, or third time a relative had arrived from the village."

"Then in an instant, five men burst into the compound, forcing me to the concrete floor, kicking and punching at my helpless body without pity. They tied me up and made for the main house. I was nearly unconscious and could barely breathe. I was shocked to have been fooled and was terrified at what might be the fate of my boss, his family, and my job—after all, it was I who would be blamed for such an intrusion."

"My heart sped up, pounding harder and louder as gunshots rang out from within the house, followed by shrill cries and screams. I could faintly hear one of the men commanding my master to show them where he stored his cash so that they could grab it and be on their way before they attracted attention. I heard another robber screaming, 'Your money or your life! I said, your money or your life!'"

"Fortunately, my boss gave them his cash, and so the robbers left without harming him or his family. However, because I tried to call out, one of the robbers shot at me as they ran out the gate and sped away in their car. I was very lucky, though, for the bullet hit only my thigh and not my chest or stomach, which might have been fatal."

"I was in hospital for a few days, and after I returned in my boss's jeep, I decided that I would quit this job to be with my family, who needed me. Without me to rely on, they would have to endure much suffering and would have only grim and unhappy days to look forward to. Being a kind and generous man, my boss, to my surprise, released me from duty before the end of my contract with a bonus as well as my salary, which was sufficient to last my family about a year and half while I recovered from my injuries."

"I was inspired by the way I had been led out of this misfortune, as if by a stroke of magic, or so it seemed at the time."

"I heard an advertisement on the radio about a legal service that helped people go to foreign countries to live. I didn't hesitate for another day and visited an office downtown that offered this service. I imagined a bright and beautiful place, a place where I would encounter neither pain nor sufferings; it would be the closest experience to paradise. And with my degree, I thought only a mad employer would reject a certified, hardworking accountant such as I was. I stood tall and strong yet again, as I had done after graduating from university with my degree, guided by the illusion that I was going to launch into a career. Surely this was the opportunity I had been awaiting all these fruitless days."

"Unfortunately, however, my attempt to leave Nigeria with my family failed. The cost for all of us to go was high, and the waiting period would be very long. So my wife and I decided that it would be better if I went first, got a job, and then sent for them later. After all, if I had a job paying dollars, I would have enough to send to my wife so she and my son could live comfortably while they waited through the immigration process."

"But this was not to be; in fact, it was quite the opposite. I arrived first in Toronto, Canada. My heart was filled with joy and excitement, for here was the opportunity I had long waited for. My plan was to find a place to stay, get a job as an accountant, and begin the process of sending for my lonely family."

"Fortunately for me, I did not have difficulty finding a place to live. The son of the man for whom I had worked as a gateman happened to live in Toronto, as he was studying at a university there, and I was able to stay with him."

"Many days came and went since I had begun my job search, but I hadn't received a single favorable reply from the largest firms to the smallest. All of them said nothing but, 'You do not have the type of experience we are looking for,' or 'You must have Canadian experience first to be considered.'"

"I was shocked and devastated. Here I was, thousands of miles away from my home and my beloved family and unable to get a job as I thought I would. It was as if I had received a whole new cup filled with misfortune, except this one was much bitterer."

"Then, against my will and out of necessity, I gave into the urging of my friend, the son of my old boss, and got a job working at a general assembly warehouse as a laborer for a minimal wage. At least now I could afford to send a few dollars home to my wife. But things went from bad to worse."

"I was now familiar with this strange city that was so different from where I had come from. I had moved into a small place of my own, and I was making ends meet on my small monthly paycheck and sending what I could to my wife. However, as the days went by, so did the lonely nights, and worse, I began to get into debt. Because I needed to build up my credit, I had applied for a credit card and it was approved. Slowly I began to use it to pay for expenses such as rent and food, always telling myself that I would pay the balance each month, as, at first, the monthly payments were small. But one day I woke up to the realization that I had more on my credit card than I could pay off each month, and I could no longer pay for rent or food. I tried working two jobs, but still I couldn't pay off my credit card debt, so not knowing what to do, I began to borrow from friends and co-workers."

"Now my debt was really out of control, and I could no longer go to work and face my co-workers, who had trusted me with their hard-earned money, nor could I walk the streets of my neighborhood with my head held high, for there were also friends there to whom I was indebted."

"I had many sleepless nights, for I sometimes went to bed with an empty stomach, having had nothing to eat but meals given by charities. I had nightmares, fearful of what fate awaited my family, and I did not call my wife because I had not been able to send her money as I had done over the previous nine months. I was so ashamed."

"Then one night I arrived home to find my few possessions outside the door of my apartment, and the lock on the door had been changed. At that moment, I fully realized the reality of my misfortune. I was a stranger in a strange city with no one and no place to turn to, without any hope or will left in my soul to persevere. I took my valuable documents and turned my back on the scene, walking away with only twenty dollars in my wallet and fighting back the tears."

"Tears of self-pity fell uncontrollably as I walked through the dark alley by the apartment building. At that moment, I decided I would quit and give into God's persistent effort to see me live a poor and shameful life. I decided I would accept my fate and drift along like a leaf being blown carelessly by the wind, destined to where God would decide. All my efforts had been in vain, so why bother wasting my energy, of which I had only a little left?"

"About a year had gone by since that night, and by random chance I had ended up in the United States. Not bothering to attempt to start over, I was content to be a beggar, taking scraps from the generous people who hurriedly passed me where I sat on the always busy streets of the great city of New York. At least I had managed to escape the shame and guilt brought to me each day by the unkind words, gestures, and letters of my creditors, who now could not find me. That is the story of how I became a beggar." Then Tunde stopped his story and looked at the nurse, who had tears of sympathy in her eyes.

"What are you going to do now?" asked the nurse. "What about your beloved wife and son?"

"Indeed, a very good question. What am I to do in such a situation, which nobody but I have brought upon myself?" Silence took hold of the room for a moment. Then, before the nurse could complete another sentence, Tunde exclaimed, "Young lady, thank you for listening to my story. All that I needed was someone to listen to me to see what I need to do. Now it is clear to me. I must once again master my affairs and blame not even God for my misfortune." Then with conviction in his eyes, he turned to the nurse and said, "With your consent, I would like to request a great favor. Being the only person here, I would like you to be my witness."

The young lady nodded her head willingly in consent, saying, "I will do anything to help you; after all, you are starting from scratch with nothing."

Hearing this, the beggar, now smiling, said, "As I stand before you, I promise that I will do whatever it takes to rise above my misfortune and get my life back on the path that I had planned before. I only ask, though I am ashamed to, that you permit me to beg from you twenty dollars so that I may continue on my journey where I left off." The nurse smiled and said only that she would be back in a while, and she left the room.

Several hours later, she returned with a small Nike duffel bag in which she had put a pair of pants, a shirt, a jacket, and five ready-to-serve meal packs. She placed the bag on the bed and handed him a fifty dollar bill and a business card. He thanked her deeply for such generosity. "It is a great pleasure to help you get your life back together, although it is mostly for the sake of your little boy that I do this; after all, someone so young should not have to bear such hardship." They hugged one another and the nurse left the room.

Tunde left the hospital early in the morning. The sun was shining so brightly that he was forced to shield his eyes. Although still in some pain from his injuries, he walked, limping, as fast as he could. He remembered the brown envelope that had been given to him and was rushing back to the alley where he had carelessly tossed it.

"What could be so damn important about a book that someone who drives a Bentley decided to give me when she could have given me a couple of dollar bills, perhaps five or twenty dollars. Even fifty dollars would not have made a dent in her pocket," he thought bitterly as he recalled his experience. "And it was because of this that I was badly wounded!"

However, despite these thoughts, Tunde felt quite happy. Here he was, a determined man, looking to get his life back together and once again see the shining, beautiful face of his beloved wife and his strong young son. He thought of what his grandmother had once said to him and a group of his friends after she had told them a story: "Often, when the worst happens to you in life, it is not life punishing you; it is life pushing you to wake up." Looking back at what had happened to him since he had left his home country, he thought that this was true.

"What am I to do now? I have neither a place to rest my head nor food to eat," he thought, feeling the fifty dollar bill in his pocket and wondering what would be the best possible way to put it to use for his small hope of survival. Then he felt the business card that the nurse had given him. He pulled it out of his pocket and saw that it was for someone who worked at a homeless shelter, which was not too far from the hospital.

By now the sun was fully up, though it was often obscured by the countless office skyscrapers as he limped through the already busy New York streets. Men and women of all walks of life—young executives in well-made suits of various colors and regular office workers were all heading for work. Tunde continued toward the alley where he had thrown the envelope containing the book. He was tempted to take advantage of all the people and try to beg for a few dollars on the way, but the thought of his promise would not allow him to fall into that life once more. After all, the nurse had called him a gentleman. "What would her reaction be if she were to find me back where I had been in the not-too-distant past?" he thought. Besides the pain of guilt was really taking its toll on him, for his wife had not seen a single dime from him, and because of his shame he had not even called her. How could he even begin to explain himself to her? He knew he had to accomplish what he had first set out to do.

The brown envelope was wet and soggy, yet still intact; fortunately, the woman had chosen a sturdy padded envelope. Tunde gladdened at the site of it. "It was as though she knew that I would toss it carelessly, leaving it out for the rain," he thought. "Nevertheless, let me find out what was so important about this book." He boarded a city bus, and once settled in a seat, he took the book out of the envelope and noticed a folded piece of paper poking out from inside the cover. He pulled it out and opened it up to discover a letter.

Dear Friend,

I would like to begin first by apologizing to you. I know you expected to see a bundle of cash from one so well off as I am, but instead I decided to give you this book. Each and every day I look from my office window, which is located only a few blocks from where you sit begging, and one day I realized that I had two choices. One, I could give you money just like everybody else who is generous to you, or, two, I could help you gain the respect and honor of a well and able man in this great country that we now call our home. As you can see, I chose the latter option.

I too was once in your situation, except I was not a beggar …

"What situation could be similar to one as degrading as being a beggar?" Tunde thought as he watched the scene fall behind the bus as it sped along. He had decided that he would seek whatever help he could find until he was once again able to stand on his own two feet—starting first with the homeless shelter. He then continued reading the letter.

… I had become homeless suddenly, with nowhere to live but in my car. Being an international student, I had moved to the United States to pursue a bachelor's degree in engineering.

Just when the completion of my degree was on the horizon, I engaged in an intimate relationship with a young man, a fellow student with whom I had fallen in love. But then I found out that I was pregnant, and because my boyfriend didn't have the means to support my child and me, and he could not be bothered to make an effort to find a way to do so, he left town without notice. I intended to keep the child, for my Catholic faith forbids such an unjust act as abortion.

Because my time was limited, I decided it would be best to leave school and begin saving enough money so that neither my baby nor I would suffer.

For months things did not improve; they actually went from bad to worse. Even my father, who had been paying for my education, stopped helping me when he heard the news of my situation. He thought me a disgrace to the family and its name, as did a host of highly valued professionals in our community, including lawyers, doctors, nurses, and engineers.

But as God would have it, things finally began to get better. My best friend, on whom I could rely, allowed me to live in her home, have my baby, and once again regain my dignity and self-confidence, of which I was desperately in need.

As fate would have it, I found the book, which you now have in your possession, on her bookshelf. As I read this book, I became more and more interested with each page, and at the same time, my faith as well as my hope grew.

Seeing that the main character in the book was in a similar situation as I was, I began to take for myself the lessons from his experiences, and like magic, things began to fall into place, all thanks to my newfound inspiration.

My friend, I want you to know that, with the help of my best friend and my mother, who with forgiveness had sympathized with her only daughter and come to stay with me, I have made myself a respectable person and one of the many wealthy citizens of this country!

Truly, there is much power in the knowledge and comfort that one is not the only one in such pain. I have given you this book as a gift. I believe there is some magic (if I may call it that) in it, and my hope is that it does for you as much (or more) good as it has done for me. After all, as a great man once said, "The most powerful weapon on earth is the soul of a man on fire." And I am to this day a firm believer that no one can judge the limit to what one who is greatly inspired and motivated can accomplish. I say this not because I have seen it happen with a friend, but because it has been, and continues to be, my personal experience.

To your success,
Tracy N. Adwoa
Chairwoman and CEO
TooKute Beauty Enterprises

Tears slowly began to fall from Tunde's eyes as he folded the letter. "Could this be God finally shining upon me the light of hope for the brighter day that I have long awaited?" he thought. He did not care whether he was being watched by the other patrons on the bus; he only began to read the book ...

Part Two

The Battle Between a
Dream and Tradition

The boy's name was Toku'te. He has taken the liberty of sitting at the front entrance of his father's compound to watch the departing sun. His father's home was a small hut constructed of red mud bricks, strong enough to withstand the brutal forces of nature that were common occurrences several times a year in the village.

In front of the compound was a long narrow road along which other compounds and huts were scattered, and which eventually led to the path through the forest that led to the city and its marketplace, the king's palace, and the homes of the city dwellers.

Of major importance to the families that lived in this village were the scattered plots of farmland that were located close to the forest. For many generations, families had been living off the harvest from their farms, which, by the sacred tradition of their forefathers, were passed down from one generation to the next.

"Who do you think I am? The richest man in the city?" Toku'te's father boomed when the boy had asked for spending money. The harvest produced only enough money for the family to live on during the season when very few crops were available. Because of this, the boy eventually gave up hope, not bothering to ask his father for money to buy the sweets, which were spread out on the clean, but worn-out mats that were once bursting with color, sold by merchants, who were mostly housewives sitting in front of their husband's compound in the shade of a small canopy.

The boy's father stood six feet tall, and his skin was as dark in color as the life-giving, rich earth. He was a good-tempered man, but also very aggressive as the head of the house when it came to protecting his family from harm, and even though he was getting older, he still had the strength and courage of his younger days.

At a young age, Toku'te's father had been taught by his own father to plow the soil of their small farm, which had been in the family for many generations.

Because the life of a farmer offered very few luxuries, Toku'te and his family had to walk long distances to the marketplace at harvest time, carrying their produce on their heads, without a donkey or slaves to carry the heavy loads for them.

"A new market day is upon us," Toku'te's father said one night in a deep, commanding voice that gave the impression that there was much work to be done. "We must get up at midnight, for the road is long and the load heavy. We must arrive at dawn, or we will be stuck with an unfavorable spot at the market, and then we'd have to carry all our unsold produce home again."

Only a short time seemed to have passed before Toku'te was awakened by the roaring call of his father to get up. He slept on a mattress that his father had bought for him a long time ago at the market. It had once been comfortable, as it had been made with tightly woven dried date palm leaves and well stuffed with cotton, but now it was old and no longer a comfort to the boy's sleepy body, and he had not slept well. Toku'te did not want to get up, but he remembered what his father had said the night before and didn't want to have to carry a heavy load home again, and, on top of this, he feared that his impatient father might strike him with his cane, which was crafted of stiff leather, and the thought made him shiver, so he quickly got up.

The boy struggled to find his way around the family hut in the dark. Even though the moon was shining high in the sky, it didn't illuminate the room enough for him to see clearly. He eventually found his cloth, which he wore wrapped tightly around his body in preparation for the long day ahead.

Toku'te's father had already finished packing the goods when the boy finally made his appearance. There were four baskets. Two were packed full with fresh produce and neatly covered with pieces of fabric from worn-out clothing that were tied into place with lengths of old rope. The other two baskets were loaded with lighter produce from the harvest. There were also some extra small baskets that would be used to display the produce at the market.

The family started out shortly after midnight, the father carrying the two heavier baskets, one on his head and the other comfortably in his right hand as if it weighed no more than a small bag of rice. The boy carried the other two lighter baskets in his hands.

They walked along the path through the forest, relying on the moon to light their way over the uneven terrain. Toku'te followed closely behind his mother, who sang a pleasing song that eased his annoyance at having had to awaken from his sleep so early.

The boy had decided that it was best not to attempt to copy his mother, as she skillfully carried on her head the load of food that would feed her family that day; he feared the fury of the wet plants along the path, with which his father would beat him if he were careless enough to spill and ruin the produce in his baskets.

It became darker as they walked deeper into the forest, and they could hear the many sounds of the beasts that were awake at that hour. Among them were the owls that sat on the branches of the tall trees under which they passed. The boy shivered each time he heard them, yet he was not too afraid, for his father had brought a long spear with a blade so sharp that it would kill anything it struck.

The family traveled for a long time until finally they left the forest and came to the road that led to the marketplace. Slowly, the many men with their families came into view as they all made their way to the marketplace. Some families were large and others were just a husband and wife, all burdened with heavy loads under which their thin bodies struggled to walk.

Coming from the stream that was nearby was the usual sight of about forty slaves walking in single file carrying heavy clay pots of water that they had filled from the stream, making their way to the king's palace. These men, who had come from far-off lands, were the king's prisoners, whose lives he had spared after they had waged war against his noble city. Ahead and behind these slaves were healthy-looking guards, each wrapped down to their ankles in a colorful cloth and wearing dark brown leather sandals made of goatskin on their feet. This was the recognizable uniform of the king's servants, who were given priority and respect everywhere they went in the city, and they easily made their way through the crowd of farmers and merchants heading to the marketplace.

It was dawn when Toku'te's family arrived at the marketplace—early enough that they were able to choose one of the few good spots to display their merchandise. This spot was under a tall, wild bitter-fruit tree that provided adequate protection from the unforgiving heat of the sun. There were also many well-built shops that belonged to the wealthy merchants of the city and gave the tenants and their customers comfort and protection from the heat of the boiling sun. These wealthy merchants didn't have to worry about not getting a good spot, so their caravans would arrive just after sunrise with their many beautiful and sometimes rare goods from far-off lands. Often riding ahead of their caravans on their donkeys, the merchants were followed by about four donkeys each, walking in single file and all piled high with goods. Each merchant also had a slave to tend the tireless creatures.

The marketplace grew busier as the sun rose over the horizon. The noise became louder as shepherds, farmers, jewelers, cloth weavers, food merchants, and others began peddling their goods throughout the vast marketplace.

Much to Toku'te's joy, he had only a small load to carry back home that night. There was only a little leftover grain that they didn't sell and a few food items that they got in exchange from neighboring farmers at the market for some of their fresh produce.

"The Gods must be very pleased today, for the marketplace was full of many customers who were eager to buy and gladly spent their money in exchange for the goods we had to sell. I am very happy indeed that we do not have to carry a heavy load of unsold goods back home, for the soul of a tired body does not desire such work," said Toku'te's father to his family as they talked on the way back home from the marketplace.

When they got home, Toku'te's father ordered his wife to cook a large meal of fowl to celebrate the successful market day and honor the Gods for their generosity.

"To the Gods, to whom we are thankful for bestowing much prosperity upon us that we may rejoice in our heart," the boy's father began, raising a wooden cup of wine and extending a well-roasted fowl that was skewered onto a long, thick stick toward the temple of the Gods, which stood in the distance on the highest hill of the city beside the king's palace so that every citizen in the realm could have an unobstructed view of the temple to pay their gratitude. He continued, calling out the name of each God and saying, "Please accept from us this token of our appreciation, which we are about to enjoy in your honor." Not saying another word after what seemed to be an endless libation, he placed the fowl before the family and began to serve the meat. This was a festive evening, one that the family indulged in only once each year. Each person ate until they were satisfied and unable to move until after the food had had a chance to digest.

The moon was very high in the dark night sky, and the air was so cold that it made man and beast alike shiver. The cries and loud snoring of the wild beasts of the great forest could be heard, along with the hooting of an owl, which stayed awake at night like the sleepless maiden who lies ever awake waiting for her faithful new husband, who is long gone, having embarked on a journey on the far sea to fight the city's enemy with his fellow countrymen.

At the same time, Toku'te, who had been sleeping for only a short while, now found himself to be restless and sitting up alone in the hut. "What a very pleasant dream," he thought, as he recalled the dream he was having before he was awoken by the painful bite of a mosquito, but it was strange, because he had had the same dream only a few nights before.

The boy had had many dreams in the past, but none that he cared to remember, yet here was this dream that repeated itself in the same way each time he had it. "Curse the moment I was bitten by that insect," the boy thought as he recalled his recurring dream. "If only I could have had a chance to experience more of it."

In his dream, Toku'te was grown up and he was a very wealthy man. He lived in a manner that allowed him much more comfort than he would have as a farmer. Rather than a small hut for his family, he lived on a large estate with many servants, each performing their own specific tasks. He had three children, whom he sent to distant lands to learn the ways of wise men in the hope that they, too, would become valuable members of society. Life seemed so much more enjoyable, as he was able to go about his day doing whatever he pleased. He could travel to faraway lands and dine on rare delicacies, and he would toss coins to beggars, all this without having to worry that he would not have any money left.

The boy thought that the most pleasant part of his dream was the abundant amount of time he had to spend with his family and friends. He knew a lot about his three boys—he knew their likes and dislikes; their favorite games, which they enjoyed playing with friends in the alleys; the types of food they enjoyed; and their dreams and fears.

Toku'te was jealous of their good fortune. Unlike them, he had a father who was a very busy man who spent most of the day working on the farm, leaving him with very little idle time, and this he spent sleeping. The boy was sad. His father was too busy to make time for him. But there was nothing he could do; the boy was intimidated by his father's hot temper and he realized that he had no choice but to live as the son of a mere farmer, his mother's husband.

Finally the boy went back to sleep, and when he awoke, it was already midday and the sun was high in the sky. He felt happy, even though he had been unable to get a lot of sleep the night before, because he felt a new spirit stirring within him after his recurring dream. All day on the farm, he could not help but wonder why the Gods had sent him such a dream, and how it would be possible for the son of a farmer, with nothing but a farm to inherit from his forefathers, to make such dream a reality.

Toku'te and his father were clearing the field and harvesting the remaining crops, while his mother was busy with her household chores. Unlike the men in the village, the women did the less burdensome work; they cooked and tended to the young children who were not yet of the age to work. They often went to the stream with clay pots to fill with fresh water for cooking and to water the herbs that grew in small pots along the walls of their compound. While at the stream, each of them would also wash their husband's and children's dirty clothes, socializing at the same time in a group with other housewives. The chores took most of the day, but when they were done, the wives would sit in a circle, happily and loudly discussing family, friends, the harvest, marriage, new-born babies, and many other topics.

The most common discussion was about their sons when they would be of an age to marry and have a family of their own, acknowledging the importance of a proper education from their fathers on the art of producing a good harvest. "A newly wedded man who is unable to provide for his family makes a very unfortunate sight. This man cannot hold his head high as he walks among his fellow men, and his wife, though patient and loyal, will be greatly dissatisfied at being forced to return to her father's house," an elder of all the wives said, as she related the story of a young woman who had had such an experience. "It was as if the young woman were a widow, who, by the inability of her husband to provide a good home for her, had to return, with eyes cast down upon her dust-covered feet, to her father's house, with nothing but a modest cloth to cover her young body, and on her face a miserable look of humiliation, as she was viewed by the village as the wife of a man who could not provide a home for her. Her husband was indeed hard working, like any good husband. He labored on the farm all day, harvesting from the life-giving earth the foods that he sold for a profit. However, being an unfortunate fellow, the gaming table called his attention more strongly than his family ever did. He spent the evenings betting away all the day's profits in the hope of filling his purse at the game master's expense. And on top of all this, he spent the remaining profits on barley beer, until he became so drunk that he couldn't walk home, and the owner of the gaming house did not want to have the stay of the paying customers made uncomfortable by the presence of a drunkard, so he spent the night in the pigs' pen."

The women continued telling stories, both sorrowful and joyful, about marriages and families, until evening, when they gathered their belongings and, with their children and a clay pot balanced on their head, dispersed into the dark path through the bush to their husband's home in time to prepare dinner for the hungry men who had been laboring tirelessly all day on the farms under the hot and unforgiving rays of the sun.

The evening was just settling in as the activities at Pilo's great estate carried on. The servants of the house went about each doing his or her specific work. The women did all the cooking and cared for the garden inside the compound, while the men, as was the custom, journeyed long distances in groups of four to collect water from the river in heavy pots to ensure that there was always enough water for the needs of the estate.

Other men served in other duties, such as horsemen, who took care of the horses and drove the chariots, and collectors of firewood, which was needed in the kitchen and bakery.

After most of the work on the farm was completed, and before the harvest began again, rather than remain idle, Toku'te had been fortunate enough to get a job at the Pilo Estate as a horseman, working each day caring for the horses in the stable. The job was very demanding, and the smell of the stable, which was new to Toku'te, was not very pleasant to his nose. However, he found this work to be much more bearable than the endless work on the farm.

Toku'te enjoyed working for the master of the estate as one of the few horsemen, and recalling his dream, he felt that this was an opportunity for him to see what the life of a wealthy man was really like. He would often relive the dream and imagine what it would be like if he could walk like Master Pilo to the stable with such freedom and request in a calm and confident tone of voice that the best horse and chariot be prepared so that he could embark on a long journey the next day. And despite the fact that he was nothing but the son of a farmer who knew only about farming, and nothing about becoming wealthy, Toku'te felt a sense of hope in making such an impossible dream a reality.

Not long after the boy had begun working at the estate of the wealthy man, sorrow struck. Toku'te arrived one morning expecting to see everything going on as usual, but on this day it was still and silent, as though he had arrived at the marketplace after midnight. He entered the familiar hallway leading to the back of the estate only to find a group of servants, men and women, looking sorrowful. Some were crying, while the others comforted them, and others crouched against the wall with their head sunk between their knees. Among them, Toku'te saw a familiar face—Okale, the master's driver, who spent many days with him traveling to distant lands. He was also the one from whom Toku'te had been learning the ways to best care for the rare and expensive horses that resided in Master Pilo's stable.

The boy approached Okale, gently placing his hand on his knee. "What has happened to change the spirit of this place from the way it was only a day ago? Why do I no longer see the smiles on the faces of our fellow workers or hear their laughter as they hurry up and down the many hallways doing their work? Tell me, tell me what has happened."

Then slowly, Okale, who was only a few years older than Toku'te's father, responded, saying, "Son, have you not heard?"

"Heard what?" the boy said impatiently.

"Our good master has died. His body lies helplessly upon the bed that he shared with his wife." The boy's heart sank as he fell against the wall and slowly slipped down, crouching beside Okale.

"How could this be?" pleaded the boy, staring into the empty morning sky, which was filled with an air of sadness. "Only yesterday Master Pilo returned after five days of journeying through the vast forest to visit his brothers, and he showed no sign of sickness, only his usual kindness and enthusiasm."

The boy had not known the master very well, yet it felt as though someone close to him had died. He felt sad in his heart, and he thought about the change that the servants would have to face. Though they loved their work, it was the presence of such a man as their master that each man and woman drew joy and was able to work hard at their tasks, and now that he was gone, their jobs would never be the same.

Many days went by since the passing of their beloved master, a merchant who had been the most respected and wealthiest man in the city. The house was still full of activity, yet the spirit of happiness and enthusiasm that once existed was no longer present. Each servant went about his or her job as before, but now instead of smiles, most wore sadness on their face.

"It is not the greatest idea to burden yourselves with what has happened," Okale would say to his fellow servants. "You must not forget what the priest said only five days ago at master's burial ceremony. It was his time to move on to the underworld, so in kind consideration of the Gods, we must pray for him instead." Being the eldest of all the servants, Okale had to conceal his sadness and force himself to show a happier face as an example to the others.

Exactly one year had passed since the master's death. The estate had grown quieter. Most of the servants had left to work for other masters because there was no longer employment for them on the estate. The master's wife had decided that since they had no children to inherit the estate, it would be best to give the fortune to the priests so that they would pray for the kind consideration of the Gods toward her husband, and she left to live in her parents' home and mourn her dead husband.

One evening Toku'te arrived at the estate, which had been taken by a new master, Master Abechi, a shrewd man who neglected his servants and treated them as though they were slaves he had bought. Toku'te found Okale preparing a chariot for the master's wife, who was planning to visit her mother. "How long will you be away?" Toku'te asked Okale, who was polishing the rims of the wheels.

Okale looked up at him and replied, "Only a few days." Much had changed on the estate, and it seemed to Toku'te to have happened too quickly. There were new servants and new rules to work by, and Toku'te was going to miss the only thing that remained the same, the company of Okale, his good friend and teacher. Though the harvest season was only a few weeks away and Toku'te would be gone for a while, he still felt a sense of loneliness rush over him.

Seeing that the boy was sad, Okale did his best to comfort him. "My boy, life is full of surprises, most of which force many changes on us. You must learn to make yourself comfortable with the inevitable. After all, if you keep your sight on the door that is closing behind you, you will fail to catch the one that lies open before you. This is the only way that you will be able to cope with unexpected changes and grow stronger. I, too, very much miss the company of our master, but I would remain a bitter man if I didn't accept the fact that death is an inevitable part of life, and that it was his time to die. How else was I able to impress our new master with my great skill as a chariot driver so that he would choose to employ me instead of keeping his former driver? Had I been negative and still sad about our master's death, do you think I would have had such good fortune?" The boy shook his head.

Then Okale approached the boy and placed his hand on his head, saying in a deep voice that was somewhat forceful, yet comforting, "Son, you are the wisest of all the servants on this estate. I have a strong feeling that you will become a very wise man in your own right. For this reason, I would like to give to you a present that was given to me by our late master, who was of the kindest and most generous heart."

Saying this, Okale took something from his leather bag, which hung over his shoulder beneath his clothing, and handed it to the boy. "I found this book in my bag with a short note from Master Pilo, saying that it was the best reward he could give to a hardworking and faithful servant. It was as though he knew he was going to die the next day. And behold! Because of this book, I, a mere servant, will soon leave my position as a chariot driver to become a dealer in camels and horses."

On hearing this news, the boy had to immediately stop himself from complaining about the fact that he would soon have to work alone, recalling what Okale had said about learning to deal with life's changes. Toku'te held the book, turning it over and over. It had an odd smell, which came from its leather cover. He had seen many books, but this one was like none he had ever seen before. The leather cover was of rich quality, and the delicate pages within were bound with fine cord.

Toku'te thanked and hugged Okale, but Okale was indifferent, saying, "My boy, do not forget what I have told you, and when you read this book, you must make every effort to live by its guidelines."

It was only a day since Okale's departure, and Toku'te was sitting in the stable taking a short break. He had in hand the book that he had received from his friend. Although he was not very good at reading, he could understand most words, and he began to read.

"This is the diary of a very fortunate, yet unfortunate, man. I have indeed been very fortunate, for the Gods have entrusted me with such wealth and wisdom that I am considered among few men of such regard. Yet I am very sad because I have been unfortunate in not having an heir to my estate. Much pain do I feel knowing that my name and legacy will one day vanish from the face of this earth. I have traveled much, I have eaten the rarest of delicacies, I have married the most beautiful of all women, and I have been able to purchase anything my heart desires, yet still I do not know the joy of having a child."

Toku'te stopped reading and began to turn the pages. He was very excited to have a book that he could call his own, and better yet, one that had been given to him that had come from a very wealthy man. Only rich people could afford to own books, for the wage of an average man was enough only for basic necessities. This book, however, was not like the few other books he had been so lucky to look through. Instead of the king's laws or fairy tales, he found, as he turned from page to page, that this book consisted of short chapters that it seemed could be read in any order. The titles included "The Hardships of the Desert," "The Blessings of Wealth," "The Beautiful Daughter of the Iron Worker," and "The Burdens of a Childless Rich Man."

    As the boy skimmed from title to title, he suddenly found one that interested him greatly: "The Night I Fled the Land of My Father."

"I sit before the bright, sunny day, which yet again the Gods have delivered without fail, and I take the liberty of writing in my diary as I begin the second leg of my journey to the land of my best friend Kama, who is a dealer in fine textiles and a gold lender to the people of his city."

"Until now, I have written not of my distant past, but only of the near past, after the Gods had blessed me with the ability to amass the great fortune that I have now. It is only fair that I take the time to describe what happened in my distant past, so that the Gods may have their just reward of gratitude."

"I remember the days when I was a young man just beginning on the path of manhood. I had secured a job as an assistant to my master, who owned a large leather-crafting shop. He was very skilled at creating complex designs on goatskin water carriers, wallets, jackets, and many other goods. He was considered blessed with such ability that everyone who possessed any of his merchandise would walk with their head held high, for they could afford such well-crafted goods."

"I was one of only a few workers, and it was my job every day to clean the shop, cut the leather, and tie the large quantity of finished goods into bundles, which found their way out of the city on the many caravans that journeyed to the farthest reaches of the world. But as I became more experienced, I asked to learn more, and my master began to teach me his skills."

"In those days, I knew it was in my best interest to learn more of the craft if I expected to earn more coins; after all, I wanted to possess many of the goods that were liberally displayed throughout the market streets by many merchants, both local and foreign."

Toku'te was now sitting comfortably on a worn-out shirt, leaning against the stable wall as he read. The chapter continued …

"I am going to continue where I had left off last night. I will soon be arriving at my friend's house, and as is my habit, I shall finish what I started."

"I remember the day I had gone to see my master for an increase in pay. It was a day like any other. I realized that my income had not increased since I had become a more skilled leather craftsman. I clearly recall being distressed because my income no longer provided me with the extra money I wanted to spend."

"But I was angered by my master's response, and, as is often the nature of youth, I didn't bother to listen to his advice. He had decided that it would be hopeless and a waste to give me an increase in pay. Everything he said went in one ear and out the other."

"I had got into the bad habit of spending unwisely, and it wasn't long before I became desperate. I could barely show my face in public. I remember one night passing by the house of my uncle, who had been generous with me, but I had to avoid him because I did not have in my possession the means to repay him."

"As the Gods would have it, my master again encouraged me to take my affairs seriously, saying, 'You are young; this is your golden opportunity to build for yourself an unshakeable reputation among your fellow men.'"

"Yet, before I could accomplish the task of mastering my affairs, things took a turn for the worse. I had begun to repay my debts and slowly save a chosen number of coins with each pay, but I remember this one afternoon as though it had happened only yesterday. Following my master's instructions, I had decided to walk through the marketplace to find a useful way to spend my saved coins. But this was not to be."

Toku'te stopped to examine what looked like teardrops on the page. "The poor man had broken into tears," he thought, his interest in the diary growing with each sentence he read.

"I had decided to visit the shield-maker, when, as the shop came into view, I heard a shrill cry from what sounded like a young maiden, followed by a stampede of people, men and women, young and old, all with a look on their faces indicating that death was near."

"I looked into the distance toward the giant gates of our great city, and to my dismay, what had been impenetrable gates for many centuries had suddenly become a pathway for soldiers from another country. The gates had withstood the most violent forces of the cruelest armies, hungry to loot our city's precious treasures, which were unmatched by any other city in the world. And now, without any resistance from the city's army, which had not had enough time to get into defensive battle formation to stop the invaders, the foreign soldiers marched into our once peaceful city by the dozens—spearmen, bowmen, and swordsmen, all riding large gray horses."

"I was fortunate to have been at a distance, where I had a little time to try to escape. I remember feeling my whole body involved in the effort of making my legs run as fast as possible to escape such a horror, of which no one could predict the end. I finally came to a shop that sold animal feed, behind which was a pen full of sheep. Terrified of being captured, I dove into a pile of hay, burying myself deep inside, covering any trace of my presence."

"Looking back, I find it interesting that I, a person who not long before had looked down on the shepherd's way of life, would in desperate times seek refuge in a pile of straw meant to feed a shepherd's sheep."

"To this day, I feel the time I spent hiding in that hay pile was the most frightening time of my life. I could hear the unbearably loud cries of people fleeing, and then the instant quiet when they perhaps had been interrupted by the sharp edge of a sword or the point of an arrow. To make matters worse, the strong and suffocating smell of the thick smoke from nearby burning houses filled the air, causing me to begin coughing out loud. I was terrified and my heart filled with despair that I would be found."

"Fortunately for me and a few others, we were able to escape without any harm, except that our hearts were filled with sadness for all the men and women who were left homeless or had been killed. However, I still felt that I was the luckiest man in the world!"

"That night, I realized that this once great city, which was considered the wealthiest and it citizens the wisest, was now in the hands of merciless soldiers whose only intention was to loot her of all her great treasures, and it was forever lost. Looking back, I believe that my decision to flee the city, rather than end up a slave, or dead, killed by a blood-thirsty arrow, was not my choice at all, but it was as if the Gods had a purpose for me."

"I will forever remember my one and only master, who had been my teacher without my realizing it. I had found his helpless body lying at the entrance of his shop with three long arrows piercing his chest. The old man had died with a sword in his hand and two enemy swordsmen lying a few feet away. He must have died fighting to protect his merchandise, but in vain."

"My goal now was to leave the city and reach the city where my good friend Kama lived in his great house. And here I must end this account."

Toku'te lowered the book, and closing it, he thought, "The Gods must have greatly favored this man for him to have been able to narrowly escape death and rise to a position of prominence in a strange and unfamiliar city."

For the rest of the day, Toku'te couldn't focus completely on his tasks. Many thoughts raced through his head about what he had read, and one thing puzzled him: Surely the master would not have overlooked writing in his diary what he knew about creating wealth? The boy thought, "Maybe it was something in the diary that had inspired Okale, a servant who previously had been uneducated in the art of merchandising." Then he stopped sweeping the stable, and slapping the top of his head, he said to himself, "Of course, that must be it! Such a wealthy man would not have hesitated to put this knowledge in his personal diary; after all, he had been an ordinary member of society, just as Okale and I are."

He dropped the broom, grabbed the book again, and excitedly began to turn the pages. He came to the title "The Burdens of a Childless Rich Man," and although it did not seem to be what he was searching for, he felt a strange urging that he should read the chapter.

"Today I am sad, for yet again my wife and I have been unsuccessful at bringing a child into this world. We have tried for many years, and yet never have the walls of this house heard the cries of a baby. I sit awake in my bed at home, a building that is of a unique and beautiful design and decorated with the greatest works of art. The night is as still and quiet as the solid date palm tree that stands strong, no matter the harshest weather. There is no sound but the light breathing of my beautiful wife, who, like me, is at the gates of old age."

"Each and every night my heart cries in the darkness, hoping that one day the Gods might be so generous as to bless my wife and me with a baby. It seems that they have answered the prayers of all the others whose houses are busy with the heavy traffic of young children running around, playing and enjoying their games. I have such wealth, but without an heir, I am very much afraid that it may end up in the hands of my careless, selfish relatives, who think only for the day, not for tomorrow. But now I must sleep."

"Today I thought much of my lamentations of last night on my lack of a child to whom I could share my knowledge and entrust my wealth. However, this evening I realize that if I have learned one thing in my life so far, it is this: The Gods never fail to make into reality that which is good for each person. As result, I have decided that my wife and I will continue our effort to have a child, and I will grieve no more. In addition, I shall impart all that I have learned in this life to whoever may be so fortunate to read this book; after all, what is the use of wisdom if it remains in the depths of one's mind until death?"

Toku'te sympathized with the man, but now he felt elated in anticipation of learning how his master had amassed such wealth. "Maybe it was for the sake of people like Okale and me that things happened the way they did for my master. Yet it does not seem just that the Gods would deny such a man a child just because they thought it would be a better idea if he were to write the lessons he learned on the pages of this book," the boy thought sadly, looking at the ceiling of the stable. Turning back to the book, he continued to read.

"The night I fled the great city of my fathers, I remember first sneaking past the shop of my master, whom I had found dead with three arrows piercing his chest. I decided that, since I had nothing but the clothes I was wearing, I would take something that would remind me of how great this city had once been. The shop was dark; thick black smoke was rising from the burned leather goods that were now scattered over the floor. I could hardly see my way through such horror as I moved hastily, but cautiously, through the shop so as not to attract the unwanted attention of the enemy soldiers who stood nearby. Fearful that my opportunity of escape might be lost, I grabbed the closest item I came across and ran out through the back door, not taking a moment to examine my memento."

"I ran faster and farther than I had ever run in my whole life, flying through the open gates of the city with a leather bag containing what felt like a piece of tablet held close against my chest. This item would turn out to be a blessing, but I would go through much suffering before I realized this."

"Many years passed since my escape. I had been subjected to the random winds of fate and had been forced into slavery, and then one day after finally becoming a free man, I returned to the place, which I had carefully marked, where I had buried the memento, a broken tablet, that I had taken from my master's shop."

"For the first time I read the words scratched on the surface of the tablet. I was shocked. It had upon it the advice that my master had once given to me when I had requested an increase in pay, but at the time I had hardly listened to him. On reading the tablet, I realized that because I had neglected to heed his advice, I had suffered unnecessarily."

"Unfortunately, the tablet had been broken during the destruction by the invading soldiers, and only a part of what my master wrote remained. I will include in this diary what was written on the tablet by my master, and I will complete it with the wisdom I gained from my own experience. This is what is written on the tablet that I have before me."

Last night at the great temple of learning, which ranks in importance as the temple of the Gods, I sat in an audience before one of the city's wealthiest men. He claimed to have learned the wisdom of managing one's gold from a wise merchant, who at the time was known to be the richest man in the city. He had been commissioned by the good king's father's grandfather to teach this knowledge to all the citizens of the city.

So that I will remember what I was taught, and for the benefit of those who are yet to come, I hereby carve upon this tablet the wise words of the teacher.

One. A man with a steady income, large or small, must take care to discipline himself to save no less than ten percent of each payment of his wage. As with all new habits, he must persevere until he is accustomed to such a practice.

Two. As his savings grow in size and weight, a man must find a profitable use for it; only a miser enjoys the company of such idle savings, which eventually may be looted by robbers, or simply feed his never-ending desires.

Three. There are many wise men that live among us, all of whom will gladly share with anyone with a listening ear the many …

"And here the tablet was broken and the remaining wisdom lost. Even without the rest, however, I was content to follow the little knowledge that I had before me. Much did I endure as I tried to follow the tablet's wisdom, and what I learned I am recording here, as I believe it complements what was left of my master's inscription."

"Yet again I sit for another night beneath the dim lighting of the oil lamps in my great house, which is still a sad place without the sound of a baby's cry. Oh, how I wish to have a child who would carry on my legacy, one with whom I could converse at great length, like the many fathers I see with their children on the streets of this great city. I would give up my entire fortune to enjoy one moment of laughter with a child of my own before the end of my breathing days. Yet it seems as though I must accept the Gods' intentions; I must die a childless man."

"The man broke into tears here," Toku'te thought, as he examined traces of more teardrops on the page.

"Dear reader, you are so fortunate to be reading this diary, please forgive this old fool for placing upon you such a burden, for this is not my intention. With that, I shall continue."

The boy was amazed. Here was a man of high status who had generously volunteered to share his wisdom with a mere son of a farmer, yet here he was apologizing for a natural human response that no one would be able to suppress.

"Without a shred of doubt, I have come to believe that nothing does more to bring a man from where he is to where he desires to be than having vision. Far too many people have eyes, yet they lack vision. I do not mean the natural ability to see what lies before them, but the ability to see what lies beyond touch, sight, and logical reasoning."

"Looking back to the night after my discovery of the great wisdom inscribed on the tablet and the great suffering I endured to become what I am so blessed to be today, I realize that it was because of having vision that I was able to accomplish what I did. However, it was not vision alone that played a part, the wisdom written on the tablet as well as my own action also contributed to my success."

"Because of my vision of what I desired most, I was able to continue my trek over the hot desert sand, day and night, hoping to once again lay my gaze upon a favorable city. It helped me to build the courage and faith within myself that I needed to flee the undignified death that would surely have been my end had I given up and remained in my invaded city."

"Yet vision without action and perseverance would be an act in self-delusion. Had I not taken action and persevered, regardless of the obstacles that lay before me, I would not have been able to make a reality of my vision of successfully living by the wisdom that had been written upon the tablet, or of making a new start in a new city as a capable and worthy man."

"There were many days when I thought of giving up, because without a city of my own, nor friends or family whose company I could look forward to, I felt destined to remain in such a state. Yet because the strength of my vision was growing by the moment, my will to persevere did not leave me, even when I fell into the worst of all my misfortunes."

"Here is a short tale that a friend once told me when we were young men and had journeyed together through the vast and endless forests and deserts seeking refuge from the king and in search of opportunities in this great city."

Once upon a time, there was a man who lived in a city far away in the east. As was the tradition in this strange city, men were accustomed to marrying up to four wives if they possessed the means to provide for them equally.

One night the man suddenly fell ill and was on his death bed. He was nearing old age, and it was a time when he should have been occupied with such tasks as the approving or disapproving of suitors who came to ask for the hand in marriage of one of his many daughters.

Many days came and went as the man lay helpless on his bed, for the sickness only became worse. Then one night he was awakened by what seemed to be a nightmare; he saw his wives and their children engaged in an endless battle over the sharing of his possessions, especially a large bag of gold that he had been saving to help his eight sons make a start at a profitable enterprise. Apparently the family was plotting against each other; some had employed criminals to murder others, while others had used means such as black magic to gain a favorable position in the division of his treasure.

Realizing that despite the will of record that he had written, it would not prevent a disastrous end from coming to pass, so he decided that it would be best to hide his gold away from his family's greedy and unjust hands. So one night while he was visiting his aging mother for the last time, and with all the strength he could summon, he went out in the middle of the night and buried the gold deep in the desert beneath a date palm tree at one of the desert's many oases.

Many years would pass, but no one ever learned about the hidden treasure until one day when the eldest wife found among her small share of her late husband's belongings a small leather bag that contained a piece of gold and a diagram that appeared to be a map.

In secret she shared her discovery with her only son, who instantly understood its significance and immediately left the city with his slave in search of the treasure for his mother, for she was now in the grips of old age and could not have gone by herself.

The son searched for many days and months, traveling from one oasis to the next in the sweltering desert with nothing but hope. The only thing that kept him going was the thought of the carefree lifestyle he could enjoy and the ability to have all the things he could only dream of having on the wage he earned.

Then one day when he and his slave were digging fruitlessly at yet another date palm tree, the man struck the base of the tree angrily with his shovel, cursing in bitter remorse for having wasted so much time searching for something that he was not even sure existed. Disillusioned, he ended his search and ordered his slave to gather their belongings, and they left.

However, the slave, having himself had a vision of how life could be if he were a free man, decided to continue to search for the treasure; after all, he had nothing to lose but a whole lot to gain. So for two weeks he sneaked out in the middle of the night and continued to dig at the base of the palm trees, covering his trail as he went. And then one night he struck a hard surface. "The gold! The gold!" he cried out softly so as not to attract any unwanted guest who would gladly take all of his treasure and leave him a slave with nothing.

As fate would have it, the slave had found the gold buried only four palm trees from where his master had decided to give up digging.

"Fearful that I, too, could be a victim of such regret at losing what I had been seeking, I kept this tale at the back of my mind to remind me of the man who had given up only four date palm trees from the gold he had been seeking for years."

The man's tale had ended and night was just settling in as the light followed the sun over the edge of the earth, leaving nothing but the moon and the stars to carry the burden of lighting the darkness.

Because Toku'te had spent most of his time reading the diary, he had fallen behind in his work, and so to avoid the wrath of Master Abechi, who was easily angered by the laziness of his servants, he had decided to stay late, working hard to finish cleaning the stable before the master's inspection the next morning, so it was dark when he was ready to leave the house of his master to return home.

As he walked home alone along the forest path, Toku'te turned over and over in his mind all he had read in the dead man's diary. "Could this be the workings of the Gods, leading me down a path that only they are familiar with?" he thought. The night was very still and silent, with nothing but the sounds of the forest beasts caught in a deep slumber. Toku'te walked cautiously, with only the pale light from the moon through the trees that lined the path to guide him; however, his attempt at being courageous slowly faded away as the sounds of the forest seemed to draw closer and closer. But he hoped that if he were to be chased by a wild beast, he would be able to escape by climbing to the top of a tree before he fell victim to the merciless jaws of a beast that was only trying to escape its worst enemy—an empty stomach.

Although Toku'te would be very late arriving home, he did not fear the anger of his father, who was as protective as he was strict. It did not matter to him if he were not pleased with him for coming home late. "If my father decided to beat me," he thought, "the pain of the whip would seem to be well worth it; after all, my reason for being so late is a worthy one. I could not in a thousand years read such a book in the presence of my father, he would never understand. He would say, 'Why does a farmer need to read a book?' Though a strong man, my father is overly concerned about every possible thing that could go wrong—either a robber could kidnap me and sell me as a slave in a strange city, or I could be executed as a sacrifice by the priests who performed black magic in return for a large sum of gold that they would garner with very little effort."

Finally, he arrived home and slowly opened the door, which was made of five vertical timber boards, and slipped inside. He was in luck, as his family was sound asleep, especially his father, who lay by the entrance to the hut, snoring deeply, his mouth opening and closing rhythmically, which was humorous to see. Within reach, as always, was his spear, concealed from the view of any intruder, whom he would strike without a moment's hesitation.

"Such protection is not necessary. The city and its realm are well protected by the king's army, which stands guard around and on top of the city's tall, thick walls with arms at the ready. But then again, an extra level of protection may be necessary, as no one can predict what will happen tomorrow," thought the boy as he recalled the story of his late master, who had found his employer had been killed while fighting to defend his wares from the invading army.

Eager to take his first step toward the realization of his dream, Toku'te had worked diligently for his master, taking good care of his horses, feeding them, and cleaning out the stable regularly, and he had made a habit of saving a part of his wages and protecting his savings diligently. When he arrived home, he did not lie down to sleep until he had found a storage place for his treasure, which he kept in a worn pouch that he had carefully mended so that all the holes were sealed, and he had added a strap so he could wear it around his neck concealed beneath his clothing.

Toku'te was now home to stay for the harvest season. Recently, while working at Master Abechi's stable, he had become used to working alone, as his friend Okale had left to pursue the life of a horse and camel merchant. Now he and his father worked hard on the farm, the sun beating down on them from a clear sky with few clouds to provide shade. The harvest work was demanding and there was much to be done in a short time. Market day was only five days away, and it would be unfortunate indeed if they missed this opportunity to sell their produce and earn a substantial profit. This market day was a special once-a-year occasion, when many foreign merchants came to the city and would spend their money liberally on local goods. Other market days would bring in only a small profit, for which the farmers had to be content, as the only buyers were mostly the local farming families who would bargain with one another with the little money they had.

Market day was busy, Toku'te and his family set up their stall. By midday, when the sun was at its highest, Toku'te decided to take a walk around the market to see the other wares. Merchants from faraway cities were displaying their wares, and Toku'te was dazzled as he walked along the narrow pathways lined with stalls displaying such goods as he had never seen before. He saw strange clothing—robes lined with designs made with golden threads and leather sandals that would cover much of the foot, unlike any he had ever seen before. "With such luxurious sandals, I could walk comfortably on the hot sand or along the forest path without fear of hurting my feet," he thought. In his excitement, he vowed that one day he would buy sandals like these, but for now, he didn't have the money for them, and he was hesitant about spending his savings.

All day Toku'te could not help thinking about possessing a pair of those sandals, and what was worse was that his desire was made more urgent because the merchant had told him that he had only five pairs left and he would not be returning to the city until the big market day in a year's time.

As the marketplace grew quieter, Toku'te became more anxious and desperate. "What if the man did not return the next year?" he asked himself. "I would lose the chance of owning such perfect sandals. Even if other merchants would be selling sandals, none would be as well crafted as these ones." He felt the pouch containing his savings, which he wore concealed under his clothing, and thought, "Maybe I ought to buy those sandals! After all, I do have enough money."

After a short battle within his mind, trying to convince his disciplined self to make the purchase, he decided that he would buy the sandals. "I can begin saving again; after all, I am good at saving now and it will be easy enough to do."

So Toku'te ran to the stall displaying the sandals and paid for them, saying to himself, "I can replace this money by adding an extra amount to my savings from the next payment of my wages."

But after a month, Toku'te woke one morning to the reality of the situation. "What a disaster!" he thought angrily, "I am a fool! How could I have been so carried away by my desire to spend my only savings on something that I could have purchased at another time?" A friend had also told him that the merchant always returned each year with better merchandise than the year before. The boy's heart was bitter too, because the pouch in which he carried his treasure was so light compared with the past when it was heavy with the weight of his savings. He promised himself that the next time he would not be so foolish as to allow himself to fall victim to his desire. Thus, he decided it would be best to leave the pouch at home, hidden in a place where it would be secure from wandering hands and eyes. He also wore the sandals around to serve as a painful reminder of how he had fallen victim to his desire at the cost of his savings.

Delighted that he was now back working for his wealthy master, Toku'te began again to save a part of his wages. Only this time he did so with greater effort and discipline, placing into his pouch the promised portion before he spent any part of his wage. Many weeks went by in this way.

At this time, there was still work to do on the farm to prepare for the coming planting season, and Toku'te had to help his father a few days a week; he spent the remaining days working at Master Abechi's stable.

One morning after working late at the stable the night before, Toku'te was awakened by the screaming voice of his father ringing out in the early morning air, telling him to get up at once. He had no choice but to get up, but he wished he didn't have to because his body still needed much sleep. "Toku'te!" his father yelled again impatiently when Toku'te still didn't appear. "Boy, get up at once, the sun is up and there is much work for us to do on the farm. It is a lazy man who sleeps long past sunrise!"

"Son, you are at the gates of manhood," Toku'te's father began, stopping to observe him after he had securely loaded the donkey with the big basket of kindling for the fire, which the housewives would buy. The day at the farm had been long and tiring; however, the father and son were fortunate to have been favored by a softly blowing breeze and clouds that dominated the sun for most of the day, creating a comfortable shade. The boy's father continued, "On your journey to manhood, you must be well prepared to meet your responsibilities, for unfortunate is he who cannot meet his obligations. My son, you have been a good student to your father. You have worked diligently on the farm season after season, learning the necessary skills that every farmer must know well. Thus, you are prepared to take over this farm of your forefathers, and in doing so you will be able to provide food and a living for yourself and your family without fear of unemployment. You will sleep soundly at night, for you will be secure in having a dependable livelihood." Then, with a smile on his face, he looked at the boy and asked, "What do you say, my son? Are you not happy?"

The image of his recurring dream flashed on to the screen of his mind, reminding him of the possibility of life as a prosperous man, and he found himself comparing this with the life of a farmer like his father and his forefathers. He immediately felt an inner conviction that spending the rest of his days on the farm, selling the harvest for a small amount that his family would have to be content with, was not to be his destiny. He very much favored a life of prosperity, where he would not be burdened with the constant need to work on the farm, or in the stable for that matter. He wanted a life where he could choose to spend as much time with his wife and children and his fellow men as he wished, sharing wisdom and stories; travel for days to strange and unfamiliar cities for leisure without the fear of some sort of scarcity; or help those who were less fortunate than he.

Fearful of his father's reaction if he told him that he did not wish to follow the ways of his forefathers and the rest of their society in the tradition of living off the farm, he said, "I am indeed privileged to have been your student, Father. I have learned much from you about farming, and I am confident that my family would not be hungry, and I agree with you, such a source of livelihood would offer such security that any man could depend on it."

Although he spoke cheerfully, Toku'te's heart sank as he thought to himself, "Here is a father trying to ensure that his only son is well and able, when he becomes a man with a family of his own, to follow the path that he had taken for so many years, yet here I am rejecting what I truly desire and lying to my own father. Ah, I am a stranger in a strange land! How I wish that the Gods did not send to me such a cruel dream. How did they expect me, a mere son of a farmer, to navigate a path to such a grand destination? How am I supposed to tell my father that I no longer wish to walk this path, despite all his years of hard work and happiness at having been a good teacher to his son in the ways of his ancestors? Oh, such cruel fate!" the boy cried from his heart. "What have I done to deserve such a cruel fate? I am innocent of any sins, and besides, I am only a boy."

That evening, as the sun was setting, the boy and his father began their journey home with the loaded donkey. Toku'te walked behind the ass, beating it with a stick when it slowed down or veered off the path, and his father walked in front, holding the rope that was tied to the donkey, and led the way. The boy's mind was filled with all the possible ways he could tell his father about his decision to follow his dream, but the fear of what his father would do or say made him shiver. His father was a man of tradition who could not and would not tolerate such change.

No longer bearable, and realizing that if he were to follow his father's advice and pursue the life of a farmer at the sacrifice of his dream, he would forever be doomed to an unhappy and unfulfilled life, Toku'te gathered all the courage he could summon and said, "Father, you are a good man, you have taught me the fine art of farming so that I too may become a farmer like you, able to provide a comfortable life for my own family."

His father smiled as he looked back at his son with a look that showed satisfaction. The boy's heart sank, for here was a man who rarely smiled, smiling. The last thing on the boy's mind was to say anything that would turn that smile into a frown. Toku'te remained silent, against his will, for the rest of their journey home.

That night Toku'te tossed and turned and hardly slept. Thoughts of how to tell his father about his chosen path kept erupting in his sleepless mind, like a river flowing continually over the falls. Not knowing what to do, the boy decided it would be best to seek the advice of his mother. After all, she had told him in the past that he could talk to her about anything, and she had a more favorable temper than his father.

Toku'te slipped over to where his mother lay asleep and nudged her until she awoke. Being of a calm nature, the woman smiled and immediately asked what was wrong. The boy's mother led him out of the family's cramped hut, taking care not to wake the old man, who would spill out an endless stream of curses on anyone who was careless enough to waken his tired soul. As it was with some nights, the full moon was large and shone like a great ball of silver in the night sky, bright enough to make the dew on the plants sparkle.

"My son," his mother began, placing her hand on her son's cheek, "Your face holds the look of one on whom much unhappiness has fallen. Tell your mother what is bothering you, so that I may help you conquer your worry, a worry seems so great that it would consume the heart of any mother."

"Mother," the boy began slowly, still fearful of her reaction, "you are a great mother and I have no intention to cause you any worry. I am in much conflict with the expectations of my father and that of our tradition, and I don't know what to do." His mother listened patiently, yet eagerly, to her son, unlike his father, who after hearing anything that he disagreed with, would interrupt without listening further and without remorse or any consideration. "I do not wish to follow the path of my ancestors and the many other people who live in this village," Toku'te continued cautiously, making sure to break eye contact with his mother.

There was complete silence and Toku'te could feel the tension in the air, "Oh, what have I done?" he asked himself regretfully. "Maybe my own mother is not as I had thought she was; maybe she is like my father and tied to tradition."

"Why do you talk like this, my son? What has become of your desire and enthusiasm to become a farmer like your father? What would you do instead?"

The boy was amazed. His mother was calm and seemed to understand and wanted to listen. "Mother, I am confident in my ability to make a successful life as a farmer like my father, raising good, healthy crops from the dark earth, which any man would be delighted to harvest to sell for a large profit on market day, and thus support his family. Yet I am even more confident that the Gods do not intend this to be my path."

"What path do you consider to be more important than the tradition of your ancestors, which for many generations has served us well?"

With a sigh of relief, yet still being cautious, Toku'te said, "Mother, I very much desire the path that the Gods have shown to me through a recurring dream that they have sent to me while I slept. I want to take a path whereby a man can be prosperous and provide for his family without spending all day and night working on a farm and going to the marketplace, giving nothing to his good family but an unfulfilled life. On this path a man can spend more valuable time with his good wife and children, teaching them wisdom, and he can build the Gods vast temples to honor them and the names of his parents. Such a path would allow a man to have an endless stream of gold that he may travel to far-off lands and give generously to those who are less fortunate."

"A good life that would be, indeed, my son. You would have a very happy wife if you spent long hours giving her the attention that so many wives crave from their husbands, who are so busy working on the farm or at the market," his mother said, grabbing the hand of her ambitious son. "Son, you possess a worthy ambition, and I have no ill feelings toward you for wanting to take this path. I am your mother, and it is my daily prayer that you pursue whatever makes you a happy man."

"I have never told you this, son, but I too was an ambitious young maiden. I wanted to be a weaver of colorful garments so beautiful that all the maidens of this great realm and in far-off lands could be beautifully dressed in clothing that would enhance the beauty that is common in all maidens on their sacred day—the day of their wedding. However, as tradition dictated, my father would not allow me to follow my wish, saying, 'A woman must not put anything above her duty to her husband and family. A woman who does so is favored less by the Gods, for she would make her family unhappy.'"

"To my regret I did not follow my heart, I married without the hope that I might one day pursue what I most desired …" Toku'te's mother stopped as she struggled to complete her sentence with tears falling from her eyes. "Yet grateful I am to the Gods for blessing this family with such a young man as you, my son, and it was well worth the sacrifice of my dream to have the Gods bless me with you as a son—a much more important gift. You must do as your heart desires; the pain of regret for letting an opportunity to make a new start go by can be too much to bear."

The boy smiled and leaned over and kissed his mother on her forehead, which bore the shallow lines of approaching old age.

The morning slowly brightened as the sun crawled up from the horizon, signaling a new day. Gradually the nearby forest came alive with birdsong and the cries of the large beasts. Soon the boy's father, coughing and clearing his throat as he did every morning, made his appearance before the two who had been sitting outside on a straw mat. Toku'te sat up straight when he saw his father, not out of respect, but because he was startled.

Toku'te's father was surprised to see the two sleepless souls, and he said, "A body that lacks the goodness of sleep is useless, for he accomplishes nothing worthy during the day, and only wastes valuable time."

The boy's mother got up to prepare breakfast while the boy remained seated a little longer, thinking, yet again, about how to approach his father regarding his decision, and shivering in fear of the man's unknown reaction.

"Father," said Toku'te with a sudden surge of courage, as he walked toward his father, "You are the best father any young man could wish to have, for you have passed on your wisdom to me so that I too, like you, will be a successful farmer and be able to provide for a growing family and stand well among my fellow men, and for that I thank you." The boy thought it was a good idea to praise him first and brighten his mood so that he may have a greater chance at getting a favorable reaction, yet he was finding this to be more difficult than he ever imagined it would be. His heart was racing as fast as if he were running to escape capture by a group of robbers who wanted to sell him as a slave.

"Yet, Father," the boy continued after a short pause, "as fortunate as I am to inherit the farm of my great forefathers, I believe it would be wiser if I were to follow my heart's desires." At this point, Toku'te's mother peeked out of the doorway of the hut to observe the conversation. "My great desire is to be a merchant, one that has many enterprises, so that I may have plenty of money to provide for and raise a happy family, and so that, like you, I will be able to be a good father to my son."

Suddenly the boy had a strange feeling that he should not have said this, and in confirmation of his fear, his father boomed with the greatest fury he had ever seen, "Boy! Who do you think you are? How dare you stand before me, your father, and announce so freely, without an ounce of shame in your foolish self, such insults to your ancestors! For many generations young men like you, without insulting their fathers, have provided a comfortable living for their family by following the eternally successful tradition of working hard on their family's farm from sunup till sundown to have good crops to feed their family and sell at the market for profit. What a curse it is to have an able son such as you reject his family's tradition!"

Toku'te shrank back, fearful of a slap from the dry, rough palm of his furious father. Feelings of regret and fear rushed over him, like an obstructed stream that is suddenly unblocked. Yet, strangely enough, despite this, the boy felt the strong urge to hold on to the vision of his recurring dream. It was as if the Gods were talking to him, telling him what he must do, even though he knew very little about how he, a mere farmer, could become a wealthy man. With these thoughts Toku'te felt his self-confidence rising from within as his stood before his father.

His father continued for what seemed an eternity, saying that men with much wealth are cursed, corrupt, and lazy, and that they are the greediest of all people and think nothing of taking advantage of innocent, honest, and hardworking men. Finally, he realized that nothing he could say would change the mind of his once-obedient son, so, pointing his finger toward the gate of their compound, which led out to the village and the city beyond, he said angrily, "This must be a curse from the Gods on this house, and I will not let you punish your family with your selfish desires! You must leave this house at once!"

Toku'te's mother came out of the hut and began to plead with her husband, at first calmly, but then her entreaties became louder as she knelt at the feet of her towering husband, begging him to change his mind.

The boy stood motionless. He was at war with himself, one part was screaming, "Stay! You must not leave this comfortable dwelling! A man without shelter and food is doomed! Doomed forever to unbearable hardship, and besides, what do you know about making yourself into a wealthy man? Nothing! That is what you know. If you leave, you will be a failure!" The other part was calm and relaxed. It spoke in a soft, comforting tone: "You must trust in yourself, learn from your mother's experience of lost opportunities. If you are to make your dream a reality, I beg you, heed the advice of your mother and do what she failed to do. Have courage and walk out of the compound and never look back."

Toku'te looked at his mother, who now realized that his father's mind was made up. He smiled at her, and all of a sudden she stopped weeping and smiled back at him, her courageous son. Then, with tears rolling down his cheeks, he turned away from his mother and father, went into the hut and collected a few of his belongings—a tattered robe and his small pouch of savings, and left the hut and walked slowly out of the compound.

The morning was sunny, hot, and humid, like every other day in the village during this time of the year, as the boy walked ingloriously out of the house of his father. He took the familiar path, passing the family farmland and continuing through the forest until, several hours later, he reached the outskirts of the city with the king's palace, the marketplace, and the temple of the Gods. Now that the boy would no longer be journeying back and forth from the farm to the marketplace, he realized how vast the city really was, and, as if by magic, he began to notice places that he hadn't seen before.

He was still terrified at having dishonored his father, and he was afraid that he would become a disgrace if he failed to become a well-off man among men. Feelings of regret kept rising to the surface, trying to convince him that it would be much safer if he were to return home and live in the comfort of knowing that he would have his father's honor and enough food to quell man's worst enemy—hunger—rather than wandering aimlessly through the vast city, hopeful of success that may not even exist. But again the vision of his dream appeared on the screen of his mind, reminding him that it would be wiser to press on, regardless of such doubts.

Toku'te walked through the city for a long time, raising a small cloud of dust in his worn-out leather sandals that had been mended many times, his feet shifting inside them from side to side as he walked. But this was the least of his worries; he was going to need food to eat and water to drink and a place to lay his head at night.

By evening, he arrived at what seemed to be a desirable part of the city, one that a young man like himself, the son of a farmer, could find opportunities to prosper. Not having had any food to eat since the time he left the house of his father that morning, his stomach was growling angrily as he walked down a path through a small marketplace where merchants at their stalls sold food, leather jackets, sandals, water jugs, clay pots, robes, and many other attractive things. Nothing attracted the boy more than a brightly lit eating house that he came across. It was full of the energy of people going in and out, all with aim of satisfying their hunger. The sweet aromas from the house was so appealing that they seemed to grab hold of the boy's nose and drag him through the narrow doors into the room, which was buzzing with the activity of the many attendants carrying large trays of food and others with jugs of water serving the patrons, who were seated in small, animated groups, conversing and laughing as they enjoyed the delicious meals that were set before them, while others waited impatiently with a grumpy look on their face for the server to bring them their meal.

Toku'te had no choice but to spend his savings yet again, only this time it was for a good reason, not like the time when he foolishly purchased the sandals. He knew that his money would be useless without his health and that he would need his health to make his dream a reality.

The days went by, and Toku'te was unable to find employment. He was living in a run-down shelter with holes in the roof that he found at the edge of the marketplace, but it offered him protection from harm and the cold evening winds. With only the knowledge and experience of taking care of horses and a stable, and the useless skill of farming, the boy had not found work after ten days of searching. By then his pouch of savings was empty and he grew desperate and afraid that he would die of starvation and thirst. He had turned his back on everyone in his past, including Master Abechi, sure that he would find work that was more suitable to one who was moving up in the world, and after not showing up to work for so many days, Toku'te was too ashamed to return and ask to have his old job back.

One morning, he made himself look as presentable as possible, although without much success, and made his way to a stable that was located in the middle of the marketplace. Turning over in his mind what he would say to the owner to persuade him to grant him employment, Toku'te hurried the short distance through the already busy marketplace to the stable, where he found the proprietor busy getting ready for the day's trading. Toku'te approached the man and said, "Please do not judge me by my appearance, but by my desire to learn your expert skills in tending horses. I am an eager and disciplined learner who would make a dutiful and hardworking assistant who could take on many of your burdensome tasks, allowing you to have more time to rest during your busy days. To prove this to you, with your permission, I am prepared to work for you today without pay."

The proprietor thought the boy was very strange, here he was looking as dirty as a beggar, and yet he had asked not for leftover food or some change, but for employment.

The two were silent for a short while, the man looking at the boy in surprise with his hands on his hips, trying to figure out what he was up to. "I don't know what to say, young man, but since you seem to have such a clear picture of what you want, you shall have it. It is often wiser to take things as they are and not overanalyze them. You can work here in my stable for the day, as you have offered, and I will see how you do; after all, actions speak louder than words."

The boy's stomach growled all day long as he cleaned the rows of stalls in the stable, shoveling manure and scrubbing the floor clean. He was determined to please this man, who had given him a chance, in the hope that he would once more have a steady income with which to buy food.

By the end of the day, Toku'te had cleaned only fifteen of the twenty stalls. He could see the man closely inspecting each stall, checking the floor for traces of manure. The stable owner observed that the boy had done in one day what it took his two assistants two days to complete. Impressed, he said to Toku'te, "Son, you are indeed a hard worker, and I am fortunate indeed that the Gods have sent you to my stable." Toku'te was very happy to hear this, as he had been nervous that the man may not hire him because he hadn't finished cleaning all the stalls. "Most of the men who have worked for me have been able to clean only ten stalls in a day, and even then, there would still be manure left on the floor of the stalls," the man said, handing the boy some coins to pay him for the day's work, even though Toku'te had offered to work for free. The boy was about to protest, but he had not eaten for several days, and his empty stomach suggested that this would be a bad idea.

Toku'te thanked his new master, Master Agawa, who replied, "A job well done brings mighty good things to the one who does it. You can return tomorrow at sunrise, when we will have much work to do. The king's horseman is coming to choose some horses to buy for the king, and we must prepare them for display."

The boy was jubilant. As soon as he was out of sight of the stable, he started to skip down the road, celebrating his success as he headed back to his new-found shelter, buying a few things to eat on his way. That night as he lay on his back looking up at the stars in the sky, Toku'te contemplated what he might do with his savings when he had accumulated more coins once again. These thoughts came alive again after he had placed a part of the wage he had received from Master Agawa into his pouch. Yet thoughts of his mother kept surfacing as well, "How is she coping with my absence? I wonder if she trusts in my ability to succeed. Perhaps she lies awake at night, fearing that her only son, forced into a world of which he knows little, is unsafe." These thoughts consumed the boy and prevented him from falling asleep.

Many years had passed since the day Toku'te had left the house of his father, and every day he thought about his mother. He wanted to send her a message to let her know that he was well, but he did not want his father to know where he was living for fear of jeopardizing the progress he had made so far.

One afternoon at the stable, the king's horseman appeared once again with his assistants, as they did every year, seeking to buy the best horses. This time he saw a familiar face among the buyers. It was Agilo, the father of one of Toku'te's friends and a neighbor of his family. Agilo's family had been working at the palace for many generations, just as Toku'te's family tradition was farming. The boy felt that he could trust Agilo not to reveal his place of residence if he were to ask him to deliver a message to his mother.

Seeing that Toku'te and the customer were well acquainted, Master Agawa decided to allow Toku'te to pick out the best of the horses for this buyer, for Toku'te was by now a skilled horseman, "Besides," he thought, "to be a good salesman, you must make friends with your customers." Indeed, Toku'te proved himself very capable, as he chose a dozen of the stable's best full-grown horses, and Agilo handed over a small bag of gold in exchange

After the sale was completed, Agilo and Toku'te began to talk and Toku'te learned much about his family, especially his mother. "Your mother is happy as often as she is unhappy," Agilo told him. "She and my wife talk when they meet with all the other women at the stream and your mother has told her that you have traveled to a far-off land to tend the farm of your uncle, since he had passed into the world beneath and had no family of his own. Your mother longs to see you again, and although she has confidence in you, she is still very much afraid for you, as you are her only son." Then, looking into the boy's eyes, Agilo asked, "How do you know more about tending horses than any other farmer I have ever come across? Why are you not on the farm of your good-natured uncle, who unfortunately did not have a family of his own before passing into the world that is inescapable for all mortals?"

Toku'te sighed, realizing that the truth would be revealed. Trusting in Agilo, he proceeded to tell him all that had happened, and then he said, "Agilo, you are the father of my friend, and I trust that you will keep all that

I have told you a secret, otherwise, if the truth were to get to the wrong ears, my father's name would be disgraced."

Agilo looked at Toku'te, and placing his hand on the boy's head, sympathizing with him and admiring his courage, he said, "You are the bravest soul I have ever met. Even the men in the king's army are not as brave, for they are well off and have never had to fight battles such as the ones that you have. Traditions are good and must be respected, be it farming on one's family farm or serving the king, yet one must be permitted to pursue any worthy ambition that fulfills that which tradition requires most—a good and well-cared-for family." The two continued to talk, and Toku'te asked Agilo to pass on the message to his mother that he was well, that he always thought of her, and that she should not worry about him. Then he pulled from his small pouch a few gold coins from his earnings and asked him to take them to his mother.

Eventually, Master Agawa interrupted them so Toku'te could get back to work, and Agilo and the other buyers set out on their journey with their newly purchased horses back to the king's palace, gradually disappearing in the distance behind a cloud of dust that rose behind the caravan, which also carried leather goods, armor, saddles, and other supplies that they had bought.

Over the years that Toku'te had been working at the stable for Master Agawa, he had managed to recover the weight of his pouch with his savings, and to honor of the Gods, he had become accustomed to sacrificing a fowl at the end of each week to thank them for their good will in keeping him safe and helping him to make such good progress. He also gave generously to those less fortunate and would take a large portion of the roasted fowl for the beggars who lived on the side streets of the marketplace. One evening one of the beggars, pleased at his generosity, said to him, "May the Gods bless you who are more fortunate than we are, for it is because of good fellows like you that we beggars have any hope of receiving a hot meal."

That night Toku'te could not stop thinking about what the beggar had said. For some reason, he thought it sounded strange, and then he realized it was because he knew the man was wrong, that a man indeed has the choice to live his life the way he sees fit. "Instead of being content like the beggars to beg for my meals from men more fortunate than I, I decided otherwise. Though tough and the pain sometimes unbearable, I decided that such an end would not be my end, for I set out to make my dream a reality, and this I would do no matter the hardship," Toku'te thought to himself. He remembered the proverb his grandfather had once told him: "What matters the height you have to climb up the tree, so long as you will have food in your stomach when you get there."

"What a pity," he thought, reflecting on what the beggar had said. "Seeing a man so able as he wasting his most precious gift—time." The boy wondered if such a person ever dreamed of doing something worthwhile in his life, but there was nothing he could do. "It would be difficult to talk to a man as ignorant and lazy as he is about such a thing; after all, he seemed to be satisfied with the life he is living."

Tunde, who had been absorbed in the book, suddenly stopped reading. He was lying on his back on the bed in a room at the local shelter for the homeless. The nurse Jane had given him the card of her friend who worked there, and he now had a place to stay. He was no longer wearing the dirty, smelly clothes of a beggar, but he was clean and well groomed and had on the new pants and shirt that Jane had packed for him in the Nike duffel bag.

Tunde could relate to what Toku'te was going through, especially regarding his determination to pursue his dream, no matter the hardship. "He is in the same situation as I am," thought Tunde, feeling even more motivated to keep going so that he and his beloved family could have a better life. He was proud of himself, as he had been at the shelter less than a week and he had already gained employment as a server in the cafeteria, and he had begun to save his money so that he could get a place of his own and have money to send to his wife as he did before.

Eager to make profitable use of his savings, Toku'te's mind was consumed by thoughts of what he would do with it. He contemplated betting on the horse races, which seemed appealing; he had once heard a merchant at the eating house talking about the large sum he had won at the races. But Toku'te hesitated as he remembered the day he had foolishly wasted his savings on a pair of sandals, when he had promised himself he wouldn't make such a mistake again, and he decided it would be best to put his savings to better purpose.

One afternoon Toku'te passed by the shop of the chariot maker. This merchant was so experienced and skilled at the art of making chariots, and they were so beautiful, that even the king himself would be considered a fool if he were to buy from another merchant.

Stopping in front of the shop, Toku'te observed the chariot merchant in heated negotiation with another man, who, by his clothing, appeared to be from a foreign land. Both men had long beards and were well dressed. The foreign merchant wore a light brown robe that was embroidered so intricately that the pattern was only faintly visible from where the boy stood watching. Filled with curiosity, Toku'te found a place to sit under the shade of a tree across from the shop so he could enjoy the entertainment and see who the victor would be.

After a short while, the foreign merchant drew from underneath his robe a fat purse, bulging with gold and silver coins, while the chariot merchant called out to one of his workers at the back of the shop to come and help. The worker grabbed hold of the foreign merchant's two horses, and with the help of the buyer's slave, they attached the chariot securely to the horses.

On his way back to Master Agawa's stable, Toku'te thought about the cost of such a chariot, when suddenly, like a bolt of lighting, he was inspired with an idea. He thought, "The chariot must be very costly and only a few merchants in this city could afford such luxury for transporting their goods. I shall become the chariot lender of this city! Perhaps for a small fee, local farmers and merchants alike would not hesitate to borrow my chariots to use on busy market days."

Toku'te decided that he would use his savings to purchase his first chariot; after all, four gold coins should afford him a decent chariot from the chariot maker. As for the donkey to pull the chariot, he decided he would present a plan to his master that he could not say no to.

"Master Agawa, you are a great man; that is why the Gods have blessed you with such a profitable enterprise," the boy said as his master was hard at work skillfully crafting a saddle, which appeared to be for the king as it bore the royal emblem. The man stopped his work, and looking surprised, he turned to pay attention to the boy, who continued, "But it is my desire to make your enterprises even more profitable. I have an idea for a way to use the idle donkeys that do nothing but lie in the shade all day waiting for a buyer."

Master Agawa was a bit doubtful, but he was happy that his employee seemed much wiser than he had thought him to be. "In all my years of hiring and dismissing many young men who came to work for me, I have never known any who displayed such ingenuity as you. It must have been fate that led you to my shop seeking employment." The man paused, and then asked, "What do you have in mind?"

The boy tried his best to control his enthusiasm as he began to explain his plan. "I have had an idea for a profitable enterprise where I would lend chariots, for a small fee, to farmers and merchants to transport their heavy and delicate goods from place to place on their market days. Since I can afford only one chariot to begin my enterprise, I thought I would share my earnings with you in exchange for the use of one of your donkeys."

The boy was elated as he walked home that evening. Master Agawa had agreed to become his partner, but he would not permit him to just borrow a donkey, which he would then sell later on to one of his customers. He was an honest merchant who did not want to cheat anyone.

However, he would allow the boy to buy a donkey from him on credit, paying a small amount each time he was paid by the farmers and merchants who borrowed his chariot and the donkey until the donkey was paid for. And he would help Toku'te, at no cost, to serve his customers when they came to the stable to borrow the chariot and donkey; after all, his profits had increased since the boy began working for him.

Toku'te bought an inexpensive chariot with his savings from the chariot maker, Ozumba, and he began his enterprise out of Master Agawa's stable. One evening, after many years had passed since he had presented his plan to his master to become a chariot lender, Toku'te was leading a donkey that was hitched to a chariot into the back of his master's stable after his last customer had returned them, and he reflected on how his enterprise had become a success. Many farmers and merchants were delighted to have such a service, for it was as Toku'te had thought, none had the extra money to buy a chariot, and it would take them a long time if they were to try to save for one themselves. Many of them became loyal customers, and among them were not only local farmers and merchants, but also foreign merchants, who would leave a security to borrow a donkey and chariot whenever they bought more goods than their caravan could carry.

It hadn't been long after Toku'te had bought his first chariot before there was so much demand for his service that he had proceeded to buy more donkeys and chariots; however, it had not been easy convincing the chariot maker to sell him the chariots on credit, for this man sold only to rich men who were willing and able to pay in full.

Toku'te remembered the day he had visited the chariot maker's shop. It was morning when he had arrived, and he found him already busy at work, polishing a newly made chariot that was adorned with an elaborate pattern and studded with jewels like he had never seen before.

Two tall spearmen, each with a long spear in hand, were standing alert nearby in case robbers would try to steal the valuables. The emblem on their uniforms signified that they were in the service of the king, just as Toku'te had seen when the king's buyers came into his master's shop to buy horses. "The chariot must be the king's," he reasoned.

The chariot maker was so busy that he failed to notice Toku'te as he stood beside him watching. "That is a mighty fine chariot you have crafted. Truly, the Gods have blessed you with this skill, which is so rare in men today," said Toku'te. The merchant stopped to see who was admiring the chariot. "Ah!" the merchant exclaimed softly in a tone that showed how pleased he was to see Toku'te's familiar face, and then, as if he were a mother asking about the fate of her long-gone son, he asked, "Tell me, what have you done with the chariot I sold to you only a few weeks ago?"

"I have made profitable use of it," Toku'te replied enthusiastically.

This was not the answer the chariot merchant expected from the young man. "Hack! You have sold the chariot, haven't you?" the man burst out, and not allowing Toku'te to say a word in his defense, he continued, "I did you a favor by selling you that chariot at a bargain price, and what do you do? Sell it! Without any consideration or respect for my kindness! How dare you! Have you being so enticed by the luck of a beginner at the gaming table that without thought you made the chariot a victim of your desires?" The merchant continued ranting in this way, leaving Toku'te confused. Here he was, only trying to share his success with the man and hoping that he may agree to sell him more chariots on credit, and this man was accusing him of the faults that perhaps he had seen in more careless customers.

Finally the man stopped to clear his throat, and Toku'te seized the opportunity to speak, "I have much respect for you, and I have no wish to earn your distrust. I have not been so unfortunate to have become victim to an unfriendly gambling house, where in one night one can expect to be cleaned out at their expense by the owners of these establishments, who take away their hard-earned wages and leave them with nothing but an empty purse and many sleepless nights." The man tried to interrupt, but Toku'te insisted on speaking, "My purchase of your chariot was a profitable investment for me," he continued.

"It earns coins for me each day. I lend it to merchants and farmers to use on market days to haul their heavy goods, and they gladly pay for this service."

The chariot merchant suddenly lost the urge to speak and there was silence for a few moments. Even the guards, who had been entertained by the conversation, stood quietly. "I always know a good man when I see one," the merchant finally said in a more relaxed tone. "And you are just that, young man. The wisdom of age usually never fails to judge correctly, but once in a while it too has its faults. I must beg for your forgiveness, for I have judged you falsely, as I would any careless customer who was not faithful to my confidence."

More praise followed as Toku'te continued to describe his success with the chariot. The chariot merchant had finished polishing the chariot, which was now glowing as the rays of the sun fell on it. It stood in front of the shop where it could be admired by the customers and traveling merchants, who would spread the word of such beauty to distant lands, and the people they met would in turn seek out the chariot maker.

The merchant had led Toku'te into a guest room at the back of his shop, where a large comfortable pillow for reclining on awaited them. The room was decorated with rare ornaments made with leather and jewels, and figures carved out of wood and painted in bright colors. But what caught Toku'te's attention most was a giant skin of the most ferocious lion of the forest, from which only a few fortunate men would be able to escape. Even more intimidating was that the lion's head was attached to the skin, and it looked as though it would jump out at anyone who stared too carelessly into its big bold eyes.

Toku'te stared at the skin for a long while before he was interrupted by the nudging of the merchant, who had brought him a small tray on which was a cup of black tea with a small jar of honey beside it. He had never experienced such hospitality before—the cup of tea, the honey, the finely decorated tray—it seemed foreign to him. He was surprised that a man from his familiar city would display such unfamiliar hospitality.

"Isn't that the skin of the great lion of the forest?" Toku'te asked, pointing cautiously at the lifeless creature hanging on the wall.

"Yes indeed, a frightening sight, isn't it?"

"A little," he replied, looking from the man to the animal skin, hiding his fear so the man wouldn't think he was a coward. "How were you able to obtain the skin of such a ferocious lion to put on your wall? Were you lucky enough to find the lion already lifeless and seized the opportunity to take its skin? Many men have unfortunately lost their life after coming face to face with such a lion. Tell me," Toku'te asked, "How did the maker of such majestic chariots also have the strength to succeed at something that even the king's soldiers would have little chance of doing without enduring severe injury or, worse, death?"

Toku'te was surprised when Ozumba just began to laugh. Here was a shrewd merchant who normally looked so intimidating, and if he did smile, it was like the sun piercing through the thick, dark clouds that veil the sky. Then, without warning, tears began to roll down the man's cheeks. Toku'te couldn't believe his eyes. He had never seen an old man cry before, and worse, he didn't know what to say. "Oh, wise maker of beautiful chariots, what has come over your peaceful heart that causes you grief?" he finally asked, trying to console him. "Do tell the tale of how you came into possession of such a prize."

Ozumba smiled, slowly wiping the tears from his eyes, "Young man," he began. "Life indeed is the wisest teacher there is and always will be. I am going to tell you the tale of how I came to have such a magnificent lion hanging harmlessly on the wall of this room, which by the glory of the Gods I was able to build." The man paused to take a sip from the delicately designed cup that held the hot black tea, while Toku'te made himself more comfortable on the large pillow they were sitting on. He was very anxious to learn how a man like him, a chariot maker with no combat training had defeated such a ferocious animal.

"A very long time ago," Ozumba began, speaking in a deep voice that drew the young man in. "Many years before you were born, when I was but a young lad, I lived with my good family at the house of my father in the great city of Dellas, a city so far away from here that a year's journey, even with the swiftest horses, would not be long enough to reach it. Dellas was unlike the cities we know here, as every profession you could think of could be found there. For this reason, the city prospered from its trade with merchants from many other lands. There were farmers, steelworkers, loggers, shepherds, camel traders, bakers, butchers, leather tanners, and many more, who sold their goods to foreign merchants."

"My father was a firewood merchant. He earned his living collecting and selling wood needed by families to build fires to prepare nourishing meals, and to iron ore smelters to keep the hot fire going day and night, where the iron workers, who once had fair complexions, now had blackened arms and faces and many scars on their skin."

"As was the case with most families, except the king and the rich merchants of the city, my family lived moderately. With the little income my father earned from the sale of firewood, we had enough food and didn't go hungry, and we were able to wear presentable clothing."

"My mother was a gentle and loving soul who unfailingly took good care of her family. Every day she would walk with a heavy clay pot on her head along the path through the wide open savannah to the river, where she would collect water to cook with and for the family to drink."

Toku'te thought about his own mother and how much he loved her for her generosity, kindness, and care. "Mothers must be the Gods' favorite creation," he thought, "whereas fathers, even though they are also caring and protect their family from harm, seem evil with their deafening yelling and their unyielding obligation to traditions that no longer have meaning."

Toku'te continued to listen to Ozumba, trying his best to forget about the day he was forced to leave home. "As the years went by," Ozumba continued, "I was no longer interested in going with my mother to the river to fetch water or wash the dirty clothes, and I outgrew the children's tales that she would tell me. Instead I became interested in my father's work of chopping wood, putting it into piles, and bundling it up and loading it on the wagon to sell to the many buyers in the city, among whom was the king himself."

"On one bright sunny day in the city, there was much energy and excitement in the air. The aroma of delicious dishes from the surrounding houses filled the air—meat frying in hot oil or roasting over an open fire, a variety of soups, and cornmeal—reassuring my grumbling stomach that once again another festival had arrived."

"This was the annual festival of the Gods, a day in which the king, together with his subjects, gave thanks for a fruitful harvest. Each family would cook a variety of dishes to contribute to the many foods brought to the city square where the festivities were held. The festivities were so grand that the people felt that they were favored by the Gods, and no one wanted the day to end. Besides the delicious food, there would be the king's parade, magicians, acrobats, drumming, singing, and dancing."

"On the day before the festival, my father and I were so busy that we couldn't take a moment to rest. Everyone needed more firewood, including the baker to keep his oven hot long enough to bake all the needed bread, and the women to cook the delicious dishes that would make a favorable impression on the citizens. Yet of all these people, the king purchased the most firewood. According to tradition, he was responsible for making sacrifices to honor the Gods that protect his city and make it prosper with a good harvest. Thus, one hundred fat sheep would be sacrificed and roasted in the middle of the city square so that each citizen, from the youngest to the oldest, could enjoy the food to their heart's content, and they, too, would surely be thankful to the Gods."

"My father and I were still busy as the day came to a close, with the sun, a great ball of fire, slipping behind the wall of the horizon. The marketplace had become quieter, as most of the preparations for the festival the next day had been completed and people were no longer hurrying up and down the dusty roads. I followed my father along the broad roadway that led into the king's palace. Leaving the palace were many men taking the implements needed for the sacrifices to the Gods to the marketplace; some carried long sharp knives, others carried large pots of spices, herbs, and water. Inside the palace, my father and I caught a glimpse of the king engaged in conversation with a group of men, who, according to my father, were the men whose opinions and judgment the king relied on when conducting the affairs of the city."

"We waited as the king had requested through his servant, a young man dressed in a beautiful cloth wrapped around his body, richly embroidered with the royal emblem. The king took such pride in the festivities that he would allow no one but himself to pay for the firewood that would be used to honor the Gods."

"We sat in the palace parlor amidst the loud activity of the servants as they hurried about preparing for the festivities. We were seated on a vast carpet that covered the entire floor. The carpet was woven in intricate patterns of gold, red, white, green, and black. It was a work of art that must have taken months of work by the most experienced and talented weavers. The king's emblem, the royal lion, was woven into the center of the carpet. It was stunning in its detail, with the hair of its mane and sharp claws vividly portrayed. Underneath the emblem were some words that I could not read with my limited knowledge, but my father told me that they said Courage, Honor, and Integrity."

"After a short while, a young man dressed in an exquisite uniform appeared before us. He wore finely crafted leather sandals that looked new, and which had the same emblem of the royal lion embossed into the leather, and around his neck he wore a necklace of beads with small carved wooden figures inserted at intervals between the beads. He asked us to follow him and led us through a large door and down a magnificent hallway to a room where the king was seated. Never had I ever seen such grandeur in all my young life!" Ozumba said with great enthusiasm. "There sat the king himself upon a throne that was inlaid with gold and studded with colorful gemstones that shone in the light of the lanterns that lit the vast palace. The king appeared more intimidating up close. My heart began to beat faster as my father and I bowed our heads in respect and honor, as was the tradition, for the Gods had chosen him as the great king, and he was honored in this way as the Gods would be honored themselves."

"The king acknowledged our greeting in a deep, booming voice, touching each of us on the head three times with a light tap of his royal scepter, which displayed the royal emblem of the lion on its top. 'Fellow servants of the Gods,' the king began, leaning back into his throne as a uniformed servant fanned the old faithful ruler of the city. 'It is indeed a great honor that the Gods have blessed our city thus, for all merchants and travelers who visit our city say that there is no safer city than ours.' The king's eyes glowed with pride as he spoke of the city, where he was a devoted ruler to his people. 'Many years have gone by, and yet we have never had to face the wrath of an invading army, ever anxious to disturb our night's sleep. It is because of this that we must sacrifice one hundred sheep in the honor of the Gods.'"

"My father and I stood in the king's hall on an even more beautiful carpet than the previous one, and presently the same young man who had led us into the room appeared with a small leather pouch of coins, which had the distinctive tinkle of gold coins. The king stood to take the leather bag. 'Thank you, good chancellor,' he boomed at the young man, who bowed and stepped aside, taking a position to the left of the throne. When the king was seated, he seemed of normal stature, but when he stood up, he was taller than anyone I had ever seen. 'Had the Gods chosen him because of his great height?' I wondered."

"The king adjusted the large skin that he wore draped over his shoulders. It was the same beast that was used in the royal emblem on the carpets of the palace, only this was the real skin of a lion that had once been alive, and it still had its claws attached! Though it was no longer alive and deadly, I shivered in fear as the king came closer to us to give my father the fee for the firewood. Fearful of appearing cowardly in the presence of a brave king, I avoided looking at the long, sharp claws of the creature, even though the beast was dead and powerless."

"The king handed my father the small pouch. 'In honor of the Gods,' he said. 'I give this pouch of gold to you as a payment for the much-needed firewood with which one hundred sheep will be roasted in honor of the great Gods for their generosity to my people who share with me such a great city as this.'"

"Taking the pouch from the king's hand, my father bent down and kissed the back of his hand. He was honored to be paid by the king himself, as very few people in the city enjoyed such a privilege. He said that the king was the greatest king any city could ever ask for, for it was because of him that our good family lived happily and securely within the city's walls, without fear of an invading army."

"The eyes of the king met mine as I bowed to him before my father and I departed, and I felt a cold chill run through my body. In his eyes I saw strength and kindness, yet, strangely enough, I also saw disdain in his piercing gaze. It was as though he was looking down on us, lowly firewood merchants, who were nowhere close to his level of importance or wealth and power. 'This can't be so!' I thought to myself, trying hard to think more positively about the king, who was kind and had much love for his fellow citizens."

"It was almost dark, as the sun had now fallen completely out of the sky. We left the palace through a long, narrow exterior passageway that was lit by abundant lanterns hanging from decorative iron hooks on the walls, the soft evening breeze carrying the pleasant aroma from the lanterns."

"Seeing that my father was tired after our long day, I convinced him to let me collect our wagon and unhitch our donkey from the palace stable, where it had been left with the rest of the donkeys, some of which belonged to the king's laborers. My father was happy to let me take on this final task of the day so that he could get home on his own more quickly."

"Though the way to the back of the palace where the stable was located was dark, the heavy smell of the stable guided me. 'The animals prefer to be kept in the dark,' my father had once said. To this day I don't know why that is. As I struggled to untie the knot in the rope that held the donkey to a post, I heard a soft voice saying, 'You know, such a task is much easier when you have an extra pair of hands to help you.'"

"I looked up to see who it was. I couldn't imagine why any of the servants would spare a moment of their time to help a struggling firewood merchant; they were too busy making final preparations for the festivities, and even if they weren't busy, I would have thought that they would rather spend the evening in their huts resting their tired bodies than spend it helping me. I was astounded by what I saw and couldn't say a word for a few moments. Standing before me was a young woman who was more beautiful than any woman I had ever seen in my entire life. Her brown eyes glistened as they met mine. She had black kinky hair that was twisted into tight knots on her head, and she was dressed in an exquisite top and wrap made of fabric that sparkled in the light of the small lantern that she held in her hand. The most delicate fragrance I had ever smelled drifted in the air from her body, and I felt as though I was in a most pleasant dream." Ozumba spoke of his encounter with the beautiful girl with such passion and enthusiasm.

"As we stood there gazing into each other's eyes, I felt something I had never felt before, a feeling that to this day I cannot describe to anyone. But I knew it was love. The girl smiled and asked, 'Would you like me to help you?' It was at this moment that I knew that it was not a dream; it was happening right before my doubtful eyes. She held her lantern so that I could easily untie my donkey, which I did without saying a word; it was though I had suddenly become a mute."

"Finally, in an effort to break the silence, I said, 'It is uncommon to see a young woman out on the evening before the day of the festival; most beautiful daughters are preparing themselves to arrive early the next day with their fathers to secure the best seats so the fathers can show them off to the young men of the city in the hope of attracting a suitor who will pay a rich dowry to marry her.'"

"To my amazement, I learned that the beautiful young woman was the daughter of the king. She told me that the king and her mother had had many suitors come to the palace to ask for her hand in marriage, but her father had rejected all of them, as he considered none of them to be worthy of her. We conversed for a long while about our different lives—she a princess, and I the son of a firewood merchant, until a voice called out for her to go inside."

"She described her life to me. 'Each day,' she said, 'I peer through the door of the king's hall, and I see the men who come to request my hand in marriage. Always their words and the look in their eyes reveal arrogance and dishonesty. They are all wealthy merchants whose only desire is to become king, and no doubt misuse their power and privilege if they were to become king. I am the only child and tradition forbids that a city be ruled by a queen. Indeed it is a curse being a woman, for I must marry the man who my father chooses, and nothing I could do would stop this; after all, tradition is tradition.'"

"The princess continued, 'But today when I was peeking through the door to my father's great hall, suspecting that another suitor was there, I saw you sitting there with your father, and something deep within me told me that I am to be your queen.'"

"I was shocked to hear these words. 'I am no king! I am nothing but the son of a firewood merchant who does not have the wealth, power, or ability to be the king and rule such a vast city as this,' I told her. 'Besides, your father would never accept someone such as me, a simple man of little means and inferior status.'"

"She interrupted my protest, saying. 'My mother told me once that if all else fails and there was no one to turn to, you must turn to your heart; more often than not, it will offer you sound judgment that you must follow with faith and courage, lest you be misled along a less favorable path. You are the man I have waited for all this time, and for this I am grateful to the Gods, for I am not destined to be the queen of a tyrant."'

"That night I could not sleep. The thought of marrying the princess consumed my mind. 'How is it that the Gods have planned it so?' I thought to myself. 'There are many wealthy men who would be more able to be king than I; after all, what does the son of a firewood merchant know about being a king? Maybe the Gods are playing with me. Perhaps they have nothing to do and are bored with the everyday life of us humans and they're having a little fun at my expense.'"

"Yet strangely enough, I loved the young woman and very much desired to ask for her hand, but from my experience with her father, with his piercing gaze, booming voice, and massive height draped in the skin of that deadly lion, I felt it would be a hopeless cause and defeat would be inevitable. 'I would be rejected in an instant!' I thought. 'I am not like the other suitors, who are wealthy and brave men.' I was afraid that the king's questions about my qualifications would only intimidate me, and perhaps I would be so frightened that I would look like a coward and be ashamed by much laughter and embarrassment."

"Despite my fears, I began to seize every opportunity I could to visit the princess, and after much persuasion, my father let me make the delivery of firewood to the palace that was required twice a month. Many months had passed since my first meeting with the princess, and she was occasionally able to sneak away and meet me in a secret place beyond the palace walls. She was rarely permitted to wander outside the palace grounds, and any man who wasn't a servant of the palace who was caught conversing with her would be brought before the king, and unpleasant consequences would often follow. This is exactly what happened one night when we met at our secret meeting place."

"A servant woman arrived at the palace and noticed the princess outside the walls with me. She greeted us and smiled at me, and then she suggested that the princess should return to the palace, as it was not suitable for her to be there on such a dark night. As soon as the princess had left, the expression on the servant's face changed to one of dislike and anger. 'Curse you! Who do you think you are, keeping the princess away from her bed at this late hour?" she burst out loudly and arrogantly, being cautious at the same time not to draw any attention."

"'I am only a friend and I intend no harm,' I replied in defense. 'We were doing only what good friends do, keeping one another company.'"

"The servant laughed a wicked laugh, and then, looking at me with pity, she said, 'You poor, unfortunate soul, you have truly gone mad! The princess makes no friend with your kind. The life of royalty cannot accommodate one who is of an inferior status. You are nothing but a poor boy who is trying to force his way to the throne in an effort to gain the power and wealth you could have only in your dreams. Boy, you must not be a fool! The princess has no interest in you and she never will; her only intention is to find the perfect servant to tend her shining white stallions that will pull the beautifully adorned chariot she will ride in with her newly wedded husband, who will be the king.'"

"I was sad and upset, and without uttering another word I unhitched my donkey and disappeared into the dark, leaving behind the crude woman, who continued to hurl her stinging words at me, like hot oil that splashes on the careless hand."

"I thought much of what she had said. 'Maybe the Gods really were using me for their entertainment and the princess did lie to me to manipulate me into becoming her servant.' Then realizing this was a possibility, in anger I swore never to seek the princess out again. If indeed she were truly mine, she would find a way to find me."

"One morning before sunrise and before the cock had started to crow, I heard a loud noise from the compound of my family's home. This was unusual, as it was always quiet at that early hour and rarely was anyone awake. Then I heard a deep and commanding voice say,

'We are here for your son, the one you call Ozumba. Where is he? The king requires his presence immediately!'"

"There were three men in our compound, all dressed in the royal uniform. My father, who was worried about what might be the problem, asked the men why the king wanted to see me, but to no avail. My mother, who had also awakened, was worried; I was her only child and she did not wish any ill fate to befall me."

"One of the men appeared to be a messenger, while the other two appeared to be the king's guards. They were tall and muscular, each wearing necklaces with long, sharp teeth carved out of wood strung on a leather cord, with the same emblem of the great lion's head, also carved from wood, hanging in the center. Without giving me a chance to speak to my parents, the two guards seized me by the arms, dragged me out of the compound, stuffed me into a chariot pulled by two horses, and drove me back to the palace."

"There the king was seated on the throne in his great hall, where he had welcomed my father and me not too long ago, only this time I was an unwelcome guest. On his face I saw death; it was worse than my worst nightmare, and I found myself begging in my mind for my life. I thought the Gods must certainly have been greatly entertained at the site of my demise. There I was, thrown to the ground before the king by the two guards who had bowed and stepped aside, keeping an eye on me."

"'You!' the king began, standing and pointing at me with his scepter with the lion on its top, raging with its mouth wide open, ready to strike. 'You have stepped into the lion's den with your behavior, and like the other unfortunate ones, you will be eaten without mercy! Who do you think you are, getting close to my daughter and meeting with her in the middle of the night?'"

"I was so terrified that I could not say anything. I didn't know how to even begin, let alone what to say; it was all happening too fast for me, and my fear didn't allow me to think."

"Soon my father and mother arrived at the hall, catching their breath and weeping. 'Please, good King, for the sake of the Gods, spare my son. He is my only child. He is nothing but a good fellow, and whatever he has done to wrong you, please find it in your heart to forgive him.' My father begged to no avail, for the king was furious and nothing, it seemed, would soften his heart."

"The king continued with his rant, cursing me until suddenly the princess appeared from a door behind the throne. Seeing that I had been beaten and was bleeding, she rushed over to me, and helping me to rise up to my knees, attempted to clean the blood from my lips, but her father thundered down at her and ordered that she be removed from my side instantly."

"In his fury, the king began to lay down my punishment, banishing me from the city, when the princess cried out, 'He is to be my husband!' The whole room stopped instantly and a dead silence engulfed the hall. Even my mother, who had been crying aloud, had also become quiet. 'He who is to be punished so wrongly is the man who will be my husband,' the princess continued, and began walking back to where I was kneeling, but the king signaled to the guards to hold her back."

"'A man such as he surely does not have the ability to be king. He is not worthy of such high status,' the king said sarcastically. Everyone but the princess, the queen, and my parents laughed. Some were laughing so hard that they were gasping for air, while others were bent almost to their knees. All my fears were becoming a reality. 'I reject you as my heir, not only for the sake of the citizens of this city, but also because of your inability,' continued the king. 'Besides you cannot afford the bride price that my daughter is worth, such an amount can exist only in your dreams. I will grant you two days, and then you must leave the city so that your presence will cause no more distress. You must go far beyond city gates, so far that you will be forgotten and no one will speak of you again.' Saying this, the king assumed his place on his throne and said no more. He watched as his guards dragged me out of the palace."

"Despite the grieving of his young innocent daughter and my mother, the king was unyielding. From that moment, I made up my mind about the king. He really was evil and had succeeded in fooling everyone with his kindness, making them believe he was a great king. But to avoid being disliked by the citizens, he had lied about his act of selfishness, saying, 'The Gods have favored this great city of ours by shielding it from famine and harm, therefore it is in your best interest that this man, a firewood merchant, not to be permitted to interfere in the affairs of the Gods by trying to inherit the position as king, which only those chosen by the Gods can hold. It is for this reason that I refuse to allow him to have my daughter's hand in marriage.'"

"I felt a shiver run through me as the king announced my punishment, yet I felt a strange sense of happiness come over me. I knew that the princess truly loved me and desired to be my bride, and that it had been that wicked servant girl who was evil, not the princess. But the pain of the unbearable reality that I was to wander the rest of my life in strange lands far away from the only woman I loved without any hope of ever seeing her or my family again took hold of my soul. 'Surely the Gods must be moving on to their next victim by now, for my life is now destroyed and there is not much that could be more entertaining for them,' I thought to myself as I sat up sleepless that night and tried to comfort my weeping mother and hopeless father, for there was nothing either of them could do to change the heart of the king."

"The day before I was to leave the city forever, never to return, something happened that turned out to be a blessing. It was late afternoon as I was preparing my belongings, which were only an extra body wrap, a beaded necklace carved of wood that my mother had given me in honor of her love for her son, food and water, and a piece of gold I had received from my father, who had been keeping it as part of my inheritance, when the same three men from the palace came to my family's compound once again." Not bothering to say a word to my father or mother, they came up to me and the messenger said, "You who cares not about your fellow men, come with us at once. The king demands your presence before the citizens at the city square. Take all your belongings, as this is the last time you will set your eyes on your home.'"

"The messenger ended with a cruel laugh, and the two guards joined in. They laughed until my father interrupted, saying angrily, 'May the Gods curse you for being so unjust! Have you no moral values? Instead of remorse for your ill treatment, you have the impertinence to pour salt into a fresh wound. Truly, men of honor are indeed rare in this great city of ours.'"

"'A man who has dishonored the king and his citizens deserves nothing but ill treatment, for only in this way can an example be set so that all people will see that an offense such as what this young man has committed will not be tolerated,' said one of the guards arrogantly as he held one of my arms, pulling me out of the compound as I struggled to keep a firm grip on my belongings. 'Say your last words to your hopeless son, for you will not see him again,' taunted the other guard before they disappeared out the gate of the compound."

"The city square, once the scene of the endless festivities, joy, and laughter, was now the ground on which my life there would end. I stood to the side of a large group of people—children, men and women both young and old, merchants—who had gathered in front of a large platform, all taking time from their busy day to witness the fate of the man who had wronged the king."

"'Has the king decided to humiliate me a little bit more before I depart? Or have the Gods decided to return me to my normal life in pity, having softened the unyielding heart of the king?' I wondered, choosing to disregard the latter question, as it was nothing but false hope, and I was doomed to inescapable loneliness and misery."

"A short call sounded from a trumpet, signaling the arrival of the king as he pulled up in his chariot wearing his royal uniform with the skin of the great lion over his shoulders. He and his daughter, the princess, stepped out of the chariot and climbed the stairs of the platform. The king sat on a throne-like chair and the princess sat on an elegant chair beside him facing the citizens."

"'My good people,' the king began. 'Much do I love you and I wish none of you any harm; instead, I wish for you much peace and prosperity.' To this the crowd cheered, honoring a king who cared for no one but himself. He continued, 'It appears that I have made a grave error; I have failed to see what has been right before my eyes, presented to me by the Gods. I had banished this young man in anger for interfering with the affairs of the Gods, but it is he who is to be the husband of my daughter and the sole heir to the throne of this city, your king-to-be!'"

"I suddenly felt the relief that anyone would feel after waking up from a nightmare and realizing that things were indeed in one piece. My eyes met the eyes of the princess, and she smiled at me with a beautiful smile that calmed my distressed heart."

"Having signaled for me to come up onto the platform, the king said, 'I will accept this young man as the heir to the throne and the husband of my daughter only when he has proven that he is indeed a man and that he is capable of upholding the duties to which a king who sits on this throne is obligated. He must leave for the great forest of Odulua and return in five days with the skin of the great lion, our royal emblem, with its head still attached. This will truly be the ultimate test of this man's ability, for it is only by facing such danger that we will know whether or not he is indeed a true heir to the throne.'"

"Turning to me, he said, 'Young man, I bid you well on your journey, and together with your fellow citizens and your bride–to-be, I shall await your glorious return here in the city square five days from today.'"

"The sun had already reached its highest point in the sky when I was escorted to the city gates to set out on my quest. I had nothing but a little food and water, a spear, and a knife for skinning the lion if I were so fortunate to find one and kill it."

"At the gates, the two guards bid me farewell with mockery and insults, laughing at my presumed inability. They said that I would be killed before I even had the chance to make use of my spear, for the lion was too fast for one as weak and slow as I. Instead of returning the insults, I decided to be courageous and stand tall, saying nothing as I passed through the gates. I was happy to at least have the chance to prove to the great king that I was worthy of his daughter. After all, she was all I wanted; the throne was as useless to me as a boat would be to a man in the desert."

"The possibility of death ran through my mind, for I knew nothing about the nature of this beast, except that it would tear to shreds anything that it considered to be food. Yet I felt some optimism knowing that at least I was skilled at navigating the forest path, and so I would be able to lead the lion into a trap and then thrust the spear into his heart and return honorably with my prize to my wife-to-be and my parents."

"I had traveled every day from sunup to sundown searching for a lion, but to no avail. It was not until the afternoon on the fourth day that I came face to face with the beast. It was a hot, sunny day, and the beast appeared without any warning out of nowhere. I had never seen anything like it in my life. It was unlike the image woven into the carpet, or the skin draped over the king's shoulders; this lion was much larger, coming up to here," Ozumba said, standing up and indicating a height level with his shoulders.

"A rush of fear like I had never felt before ran through my body, and my heart was pounding so hard that it felt as though it would break through my chest and flee my doomed body. The Gods must have chosen an even more exciting ending to my life than the aimless wandering of a banished man."

"My mind spoke to me of death, and then some more about death. It spoke of fleeing, because I was about to be eaten alive, when suddenly the memory of the night I had first met my bride-to-be came back to me, and instantly I felt a rush of power flow through my body. It was as though the Gods had chosen to take pity on me and help me instead of watch me perish."

"The lion was slowly closing in on me, one step at a time. Having no other choice, because the trap I had set was not close by and the beast could run much faster than I ever could, I slowly crept toward the approaching animal, determined that I would make myself the honored recipient of my bride, whom I knew feared most for my safety."

"Before I could take another step, the lion had taken a great leap toward me with its sharp claws and teeth aiming for my neck. I dove out of the way just in time and prepared my spear for another attempt by the beast, when, suddenly, it caught my leg with its long claws." Ozumba lifted his robe and showed Toku'te the long scar on his leg. "Then the lion, holding me in place with its claws, lunged for my throat with its jaws, when, fortunately, I was able to maneuver my spear into position, and at the first opportunity, I thrust it into the lion's mouth, forcing it down its throat to the back of its neck."

"The lion roared loudly as it struggled against the spear. I fled as quickly as I could, giving little thought to my injuries, fearing that the animal's companions might come to its aid, though this was unlikely, but I decided it was not worth the risk, as I knew nothing of the nature of this or any other beast."

"I climbed to the very top of the nearest tree, struggling my way up, waiting for the deafening noise to end, while keeping a close eye on my prize and keeping watch for any robbers who might come by and see an opportunity to win some unearned glory."

"Finally, the lion lay still, and I climbed down from my perch and began the gory task of skinning it."

"At the end of the next day, I returned to the city with my head held up high, proudly carrying the skin with its head attached. As I entered the city gates, the guard who had escorted me out of the city when I set off on my mission welcomed me back with a surprised and fearful look on his face. Without saying a word, he helped me to carry my burden and supported me as I limped into the city, my injury not permitting me to walk normally, even though I did my best to disregard the pain. 'What is such pain when I have passed such a challenging test?' I thought to myself."

"To my surprise, however, no one came rushing to welcome home their king-to-be, or to view the ferocious lion, which was much larger than the king's. Everyone just carried on with their activities as the market day was coming to an end."

"Overwhelmed by the pain, which was becoming unbearable, I decided I would go home first to assure my worried mother that I had survived and have my father put some healing herbs on my wounds. I took leave of the helpful guard and slowly made my way with my prize to my family's compound."

"'Curse you! Did you go mad, playing a game with the king and gambling with your life as though you have many lives? The heart of a mother can instantly become bitter with sorrow at the news that her son may be gone forever, likely to meet with death in the jaws of the ferocious lion of the great forest,' my mother said as she threw her arms around me, weeping."

"'Mother, I did not intend to cause you such bitter sorrow. You, who cared most for me, do not deserve such a fate,' I said in an effort to comfort her. 'Is it not you who taught me that I must have the courage to follow my heart's desires and see it through to its fulfillment, lest I be forever doomed to bear the burden of regrets?' My mother smiled, kissed my forehead, and looked at my prize in admiration of the majesty of nature, gasping in astonishment at the lion's long, sharp teeth and claws. She said no more; it was a though she was satisfied with what I had said."

"The city square was bursting with life when my father and I arrived the next day, and I learned that the king had arranged for his daughter to be married that day to a rich merchant who had recently come to the city from a neighboring land with the skin of a lion, for this was the sixth day and I had not presented myself with my prize to the king on the fifth day as he had ordered."

"A crowd began to gather around me as I came closer, and they welcomed me just as I had imagined they would!" Ozumba beamed with pleasure as he related the story to Toku'te.

"Despite his arrival, the marketplace continued in its usual way—loud and busy. Chariots sped by, raising much dust, sheep were bleating, and merchants and buyers negotiated loudly, each not willing to lose a profit or leave without a bargain."

"The men, women, and children were happy and excited to see me coming from a distance, but as I came closer, they became terrified at the sight of the beast I carried on my shoulders. When I reached the city square, the people cheered as I made my way to the center of the crowd, interrupting the wedding ceremony that had already begun."

"Against the will of the king, my beloved bride-to-be abandoned her wrongful partner and ran into my arms with tears running down her beautiful dark cheeks. I can recall the moment as though it had happened yesterday." Ozumba stopped and tears began to fall from his eyes once again as he looked at the skin hanging on the wall.

"Why are you crying?" Toku'te asked.

Ozumba said nothing in response, but continued his tale. "The princess looked into my eyes and said, 'I love you with all my heart and no one is more worthy of my hand than you.' That was the best moment of my life; it was as though time had stopped and the king, the suitor, and the city's citizens had disappeared forever, and it was only us, me and the only woman I had ever loved, standing as one in the middle of the city square. But I was awakened from my trance by the sight of a fat woman, whose nose was out of proportion with her ugly face and sticking out like the large beak on the colorful bird in the king's garden. She was much more hideous in daylight than she had been when I first encountered her that night outside the palace walls while I was visiting with the princess."

"I cursed her over and over as she pulled the princess from me, helpless because I was also being held by two of the king's guards. 'Surely it was because of that servant woman that I have suffered thus. Maybe it was she who told the king about our meeting, Oh, curse the moment I first met that woman,' I thought angrily."

"'My son, I am very proud of you for your accomplishment,' the king began after everyone had become quiet. 'You indeed have what it takes to be a king; after all, you have returned to the city with the skin of the ferocious lion that dwells in the great forest. I must admit, I believed very much in your ability to succeed at such a task, and I was certain that you would return to become my honored son-in-law. Yet I am deeply sad. You see, tradition requires that the suitor must return his captured prize before the end of the fifth day, or the king must choose another man whom he sees fit to uphold the role of king. And as you can see before you, this has been done. You will no longer be the heir to the throne, nor will you have my daughter's hand in marriage.'"

"Furious at such an unfair act by the king, I threw off the men holding me with such force that they fell to the ground. To this day, I am unable to explain where I found such strength. All I could think of was that I had been badly wounded and almost killed because of a stupid tradition, and the effort, humiliation, hard work, and cold sleepless nights I had spent in the forest searching for the deadly beast were all nothing but a waste of time!"

"Little did I care about becoming king. In my fury, I ran over to the king and began to beat him mercilessly with my tight fists until he fell to the ground and was bleeding from his nose and mouth. "The guards pulled me away, beating me with all their strength with their long wooden sticks and stiff leather canes. I wanted to kill him," Ozumba said angrily to Toku'te."

"I was tied up to a tree in the middle of the city square. The king had ordered this to show that I was truly an evil man who had come to destroy the affairs of the kingship and the Gods, thereby causing the city's citizens grief and distress. The king's priest announced that I was to be left out for the evil spirits to deal with, for this was the only way to save the city from such destruction."

"The night was cold and I shivered uncontrollably. However, I no longer feared death; after all, I could die honorably, knowing that I had accomplished something that only kings are capable of, and I had won the love of a woman, whom even the greatest of all kings would be delighted to have as their queen."

"The night grew darker than I had ever seen before. The lights from the nearby lanterns had gone out, and no sound but the snoring of the sleeping guards filled the air. Then suddenly I heard footsteps approaching. I did not even bother to ask who it was, for no matter what would happen next, I was a dead man anyway. It made no difference who it was, because I had no power over what the Gods wanted, and I had grown tired and irritated with their games."

"A figure slowly came closer to where I was tied up, one step at a time, taking care not to awaken the sleeping guards."

"'You are a free man,' the figure whispered softly while untying me. To my surprise, I realized that it was the princess. I felt happy, and without hesitation or any fear of the possible consequences I would face if I were to be caught, I asked her to run away with me to a faraway land where the king and his army would never find us, and where we could get married and live a peaceful life together."

"Without saying a word, she held me tightly and kissed me. She nodded in approval of my plan and we set off for the house of my father. I woke my parents and we told them of our intentions. They blessed us, saying how fortunate they were to have such a son and daughter-in-law. 'In truth, my heart is bitter to lose my only son, yet I am happy that you did not perish at the hands of such injustice,' my father said, while at the same time trying to comfort my mother, who was weeping quietly. He touched us both on the head and said some words that we did not understand, and then, joining our hands together, he hurried us on our way."

"That night the princess and I went quickly through the city gates and far into the dark, relying only on the moon to light our path. We carried nothing with us except a small amount of food, a goatskin water carrier, and a spear, which I carried for protection, and I also took with us this skin and head of the lion, which I had left at my parents' home, that you see here on my wall."

"After seeking refuge in many distant cities, we finally settled in this great city, which we now embrace as our own. And because of my experience working with my father as a firewood merchant, I had a good understanding of the different types of wood, and so I was able to gain employment helping the great chariot builder of the city, who taught me his craft before he left the city and I took over the running of his shop."

"What about the princess?" Toku'te asked. "Did you marry her, or did the king's army finally find her and take her from you?" Toku'te waited anxiously for Ozumba's response, hoping it would be positive and that he might even ask to meet her, the brave princess who was loyal to her true love, even at the risk of suffering or, worse, death.

"Our plan worked," Ozumba said. "We got married as soon as we got here, and to this day no one has come in search of us."

This was good news, but Toku'te noticed that instead of looking happy, Ozumba had a sad look on his face. "Why do you look sad?" he asked "Are you not happy that your plan was a success and you live happily with your most beloved wife?" The boy moved closer to Ozumba to comfort him.

"Son, I would not trade all the days I spent in the company of my wife for all the gold in the world. She was everything to me. But one night thirty years ago, she lay in our dimly lit, hot, and humid hut, with a group of her women friends around her, about to deliver our first child. Alas, she died in childbirth, taking our child with her. That was the worst day of my life; the Gods took her from me forever, and there was nothing I, a mere mortal, could do about it. However, in honor of her beauty, I build the most beautiful chariots, which, it is said, have no equal in the entire world."

The room was silent for a short while; only the activity of the marketplace outside could be heard. Toku'te was as sad as Ozumba; it was as though his own wife had died. He thought that it was unfair that the princess had to die and, worse, take with her their only child. "Maybe the Gods made a mistake when they let her die after she went through so much to escape an unpleasant fate at the hands of her father, who intended to give her hand to an uncaring and unloving husband," he thought.

But thinking about this for a moment, he thought that perhaps the Gods did not make a mistake after all. Maybe it was their intention that Ozumba become a skilled craftsman of chariots that could not be surpassed in their beauty. "But this is too high a price to pay!" Toku'te thought. "Surely this would be nothing but an act of selfishness."

Toku'te comforted Ozumba until he was smiling once again, and then he rose to leave.

"Before you leave," Ozumba said as Toku'te headed for the door, thanking him and looking once again at the skin that hung on the wall, "Let me tell you a thing or two more." Toku'te stopped and returned to the old man, whom he now saw in a new light as a brave man and a dear lover of the daughter of a king. "Son, life is but a mystery that one must have the courage to confront and understand. Take the immortal words that my mother once said to me, 'You must have the courage to follow your heart's desire, regardless of what anyone around you says or thinks, for if you do not, you will fall victim to the heavy burden of regret.' Do not forget the tale of the chariot maker, who had faced and defeated the most ferocious beast of the forest despite discomfort and his fear of dying and of never seeing the woman he loved ever again. Remember this the next time life tests you."

Toku'te left the chariot maker's, having secured new chariots for his growing fleet with which he would be able to fulfill the needs of his customers. He had also renewed his own faith and courage, for he had seen that the chariot maker, with only his will and wit and not the edge of a sword, had conquered what he had feared the most. He now understood how it was that a simple chariot maker could have on his wall such a rare prize from nature, a possession so noble that only kings are privileged to have.

Toku'te was walking hurriedly toward Master Agawa's stable, when a strange sound caught his attention. He turned to find out what it might be. The marketplace was always noisy, but Toku'te was accustomed to the rhythms of people chattering and selling their wares, and carts and animals making their way along the narrow roadways among the stalls and shops. This sound, though not loud, was unfamiliar.

Not too far off, Toku'te saw a beggar sitting on the ground, and he seemed to be chanting. There was something else that was strange about this beggar. Toku'te had heard many stories about men who were perfectly able, and yet they turned to begging from their fellow men for scraps to eat. Wretched were these men who had no willpower, but sat in poverty, wearing nothing but dirty old garments that had lost their color and were so tattered that it would be hopeless to try to take needle and thread to try to hold them together again. "But this man does not have those degrading characteristics that make a beggar a beggar," he thought.

The man seemed to be a little older than Toku'te's father, who must have had gray hair by then. He wore a clean white robe that was only slightly dirty from sitting by the dusty road. He also seemed to be well fed and healthy. But one thing baffled Toku'te: The man did not have a bowl in front of him in which to collect coins from generous merchants and other passersby.

His curiosity aroused, Toku'te cautiously walked closer to the man to get a better look at him. The road was crowded and he hadn't been able to see him clearly or hear what he was saying. Once he was a little closer, he saw the old man sitting cross-legged on the ground, talking to no one in particular.

"How strange," thought Toku'te. "This man must be mad to sit there like that doing nothing useful with his life but waste it talking to no one but himself. Had he suddenly become a cripple so that he was forced to sit there like this? Or is he a priest from a strange land, praying to the Gods to achieve a strange goal?"

These and other questions ran through his mind as he got closer to the man so that he could hear what he was saying. The old man was speaking very quickly for someone his age. To listen to the man more closely, Toku'te pretended to examine the fruit at a fruit merchant's stand nearby.

"There were two of them: One lived a life so carefree that he spent all he earned on the delights of good food—sumptuous feasts of roasted fowl and rare fruits. He lived for the day without giving a thought for the next day to come. The other was a miser. He did not spend his earnings, saving each coin for no apparent purpose but to feel secure and comfortable, but these feelings were just an illusion."

"Life is the greatest teacher there is and ever will be. Often we fail time and time again to become students and learn from life's great lessons; we avoid learning from the misfortunes of people who came before us, shielding ourselves from such sorrow."

"He's blind!" Toku'te exclaimed to himself, shocked as he realized the man's eyes were closed and he could not see. "Perhaps he is a beggar who lost his way to his accustomed begging spot and maybe someone gave him the clean robe out of pity." Toku'te stayed nearby, invisible to the blind man, and listened to his monologue, which was a song of praise to life, man's greatest teacher."

"The life of the first man was grand. He enjoyed the best food, clothing, wine, and women that the merchants had brought from far-off lands. One day he woke up to reality and cried out to the high heavens as he realized that he had no more money to spend. His accumulated debt had become a burden, and he could no longer pay it as he had barely enough to cover his rent, and he could put only a little food into his ever-growling stomach, which failed to allow a moment to pass without reminding him of its emptiness."

"The man was once able to walk with his head held high like the king himself, living a grand life, but now the constant pounding on his door by his creditors no longer allowed him the freedom to walk in the garments that had previously given him so much satisfaction. On top of all this, he could no longer hold his head high as he did before because of the shame of his own irresponsibility. Yet he did not know what to do, nor did he have anybody to turn to, for even his family and friends had become creditors, as he had borrowed from them to settle his debt with other creditors."

"What did he do? Well, he did what any man in his situation would do. He fled! He fled to another city in the hope of correcting his mistakes; however, as the proverb of the people of the desert says: 'Something that happens once will not happen again, but something that happens twice will surely happen a third time.' But in the affairs man and money, something need not happen twice for it to happen again; once is as good as twice."

"Money can be the cruelest master there is; it enslaves those who fall victim to its power, taking away their freedom and forcing them to labor long, tiring days just to repay their loans, or causing them to flee, only to find themselves slaves once again."

"And then there is the second man, the one who does not spend any of his wages. He is as unfortunate as the one who spends all of his. The fear of being without money is so strong that he keeps all his earnings in his leather purse, hiding it in a place that is yet to be discovered by robbers."

"The joy and comfort that one enjoys for such deeds as giving to the less fortunate or enjoying the fruits of one's labor or the fulfillment of a happy family is strange to such a man. He labors for years from sunrise to sunset worrying only about adding more to his heavy leather bag, gleaming with coins, until one day he awakes no more. And when he is gone, his family, or robbers, who discover the years of accumulated treasure, squander it without any remorse and then search for more in their unsatisfied greed."

"Surely no person willingly permits himself to fall victim to the state of either of these two men, but because of a careless nature that is so common of people, this often happens without a person's realization."

"If people truly desire to avoid an end such as that of these two men, they must live their life in moderation, taking care to enjoy the pleasures in life, while avoiding either extreme; after all, none of these have a pleasant ending." And so ended the blind man's story.

The blind man reached into his robe and pulled out a crystal bottle that contained a strange black liquid that he drank without hesitation. Toku'te leaned over to read the words engraved on the bottle, and just then the old man lowered the bottle from his mouth and calmly said in a deep voice, "I have been expecting you."

Before the man could say another word, Toku'te turned and ran away from the man as quickly as he could. He was so frightened that he ran so fast through the marketplace that some merchants thought he was a thief trying to escape his victim, and he didn't stop until he reached his master's stable. Surely he was far enough away from the strange man.

"That old man was not a priest from a strange land, nor was he a beggar. He must be a sorcerer!" Toku'te exclaimed to himself. "No one is able to see anything without eyes, unless he were a sorcerer." Toku'te stood out of view of his master behind his shop, trying to catch his breath and slow his racing heart as he recalled what had just happened.

Toku'te had great fear of sorcerers; his father had told him many stories of how they often appeared in ways that attracted the attention of young, curious people. In this way, they would capture them and disappear with them, taking them to their strange dwellings, where they would make them into slaves or, worse, use them as sacrificial victims.

"I have been expecting you," the boy recalled the words of the old man. "What could he have wanted of me to have been expecting me? How did he know who was standing before him?" Toku'te looked about him to make sure that he was still in the world of normal people, and not that of strange evil beings, peering back down the road he had taken to make sure that the man wasn't on his trail. Despite his fear, the sight of Master Agawa's shop and stable had given him a feeling of relief and security.

Many days had passed since Toku'te's meeting with the strange man. He had decided it would be safer to take another route when he went to Ozumba's shop to ensure that he would not see him again.

Toku'te's enterprise was now booming; many merchants regarded him as the chariot lender of the city. He was making more money than ever before, so much that he was able to settle his debt with his master, paying for all his donkeys in full, leaving the chariots as his only debt. The chariots were expensive, and it was better if he continued to pay for them in small installments.

Toku'te noticed a strange thing: As his success grew, so did that of the people with whom he interacted. He noticed that his master had sold more donkeys than he had ever sold before, and he was making a bigger profit from his shop. Ozumba was selling more chariots, and he was also making a bigger profit than before. All this happened because he had the courage to follow his dream of becoming a merchant. Both men had become more popular and had gained new and loyal patrons, all because his customers liked the quality of the chariots and donkeys they used.

"Surely I am justified in believing that one is not completely selfish in wanting something for himself; after all, that person's success affects the success of the people around him." Toku'te thought this was a strange idea, because it was not in his nature to think such thoughts.

He thought about the man in the blind man's song of praise to life. "That character had suffered because of his carelessness and disregard for paying his debts." Suddenly he felt happy. He had settled his debt with Master Agawa, and he owed only a small amount to the chariot maker, which he would be able to settle after a few more weeks of steady business. He smiled as he thought to himself, "I too am becoming a wise merchant, wealthy and respected among men." He thought about how far he had come to be where he was at that moment.

"Where would I be if I had chosen to stay at my father's house, ignoring my dream?" he thought. "I'd be a darned unhappy fellow, heavily burdened with the regret of not following the path that the Gods had instructed in my recurring dream. I would still be farming on that same land, only the entire farm would now be my responsibility. All that hard labor in exchange for a barely comfortable lifestyle, where a man must be content with the little money he earns from his harvest, which allows him to afford only the most inexpensive things for his family. What sort of tradition is that?"

The thought of what his life would be like if he had decided to stay at his father's house made a shiver run down his spine. He asked himself, "Why would any man choose to suffer for all his life, having only a little to show for all his hard work? It was not that it was a bad thing to work hard to provide for one's family, but that it made little sense for one to have little or no time at all for his beloved family because he must spend all day on the farm working to make sure there was food to eat."

Toku'te decided it was best to leave such a topic to the Gods, for it is they who know what is best for people.

Part Three

The Return Home

That night Toku'te sent his mother and father three pieces of gold. He had met a merchant who knew the city well and who would be visiting a friend of his who was also a friend of Toku'te's parents and lived near them. He trusted him because he was a loyal customer who rented a chariot and donkey from him twice a week to move his goods to the marketplace.

"Tell my mother I am well and that the Gods have kept me out of danger and brought me much prosperity, and that I am becoming, like many, a wise and wealthy merchant in this great city of ours. Give to her one of the three pieces of gold and give my father the remaining two pieces so that he may stop working on the farm and finally have the rest he has long deserved without the fear that my mother will be without food to eat."

Toku'te knew it was worth the attempt, but deep down he also knew that his father was not a man to rest. "A man who awakes after the full rise of the sun is a lazy man and is disliked by the ancestors," his father once said to him when he awoke late in the morning when there was little work to be done after they had returned home late the night before after a long day at the marketplace.

The sun had just fallen behind the horizon at the end of the market day, leaving behind a sky so red it looked as though it had burst into flames. The marketplace had become quieter as the merchants had taken down their tents and locked up in their sheds the things that were too heavy to take home, taking only their valuables.

The narrow roads throughout the marketplace were empty; all that remained were the footprints left by the merchants who had only a few hours earlier been busily going about their business. The only place that still showed any sign of life was the eating house, which was bursting with activity and noise.

Toku'te entered the eating house, having decided to reward himself for his hard work and the progress he had made with his enterprise. The place was bright, and Toku'te could clearly see the seated merchants waiting in anticipation for their meal to be served, while busy waiters carried large decorative clay bowls on silver trays to the hungry patrons.

The wonderful aromas made Toku'te's stomach rumble loudly, showing its impatience for a delicious meal. He found himself a place to sit and was able to choose from a leg of goat or juicy fowl, roasted with aromatic spices. There were also vegetables, fruit, rice, yams, porridge, and many other mouthwatering choices.

Toku'te ate to his heart's content. He had a whole goat leg all to himself, and wine served in a small bowl. After he was satisfied, he let out a loud and prolonged burp, which inspired groans and laughter from the other patrons, some of whom looked at him angrily, while others were simply amused by his immaturity. Toku'te remained indifferent, for he had once again satisfied his demanding stomach.

Unwilling to leave just yet, Toku'te sat in silence observing the other patrons as they conversed with the person next to them. Some spoke of their successes of the day, while others talked about the merchandise they could possibly sell with the new season on its way.

One person in particular grabbed his attention. By his clothing and age, he appeared to be one of the wise elders of the city. He wore an intricately embroidered robe that would have taken countless hours of sewing day and night. He was talking with another fellow who was similarly dressed. "I am indeed proud of my son, who has made himself a man among men. With the strong foundation of one who is able to provide for a family, the Gods have rewarded him with a beautiful young maiden whom he gladly calls his wife," he said, smiling happily.

"What a happy man he must be," thought Toku'te, looking sad as thoughts of his father came to him. "Have I stolen from my father the pride and joy that any father longs to have by following a path that was different from the one he wanted me to take?" Toku'te thought that if he could start a conversation with anyone who would talk to him it would take his mind off his pain. But he soon gave up on this idea. "It would require too much effort, and my belly is too full to move around," he thought, and instead he reclined against the large pillow that was leaning against the wall behind him.

Gradually the eating house grew quiet and Toku'te decided to leave, as the patrons were beginning to depart, some alone and others in small groups, walking through the large doors and disappearing into the dark night. Just outside the door, Toku'te heard a familiar voice and instantly knew whose it was. It was the blind man from a few days past, sitting cross-legged on the ground. His heart began to beat with an intensity that he had never experienced before. He began to regret his decision to follow his dream over tradition, for he was sure he was about to end up as a slave to a sorcerer or, worse, a victim of an unjust sacrifice. "Maybe this is what happens to a person who turns his back on the wishes of his parents. He just has to suffer the consequences," he thought in fear.

Toku'te felt a shiver run down his spine, he could not help but think that the old man had come for him; after all, sorcerers have the ability to know exactly where their victims are. He thought about running again, but the possibility of the sorcerer's overpowering him with some magic force stopped him. He was completely alone and the night was dark and quiet. If he were to be captured, this was the perfect opportunity, because no one would see what was happening and there would be little chance of anyone coming to his aid.

Terrified, Toku'te could think of nothing that he could do, and anyway, he was doomed. But then he thought, "That recurring dream—surely if I had not taken such an unknown path and abandoned the idea the night I first had the dream, I would not have made it this far, climbing a strange and unfamiliar mountain in complete darkness with nothing of value other than complete faith in myself, the Gods, and that a dream that seemed so grand and unachievable by a mere farmer could indeed be achieved."

He mustered up all the courage he could, saying to himself, "If I died right here and now, I would die a happy man, for I have been fortunate enough to break away from the limiting boundaries of tradition and have begun to discover the limitless possibilities of the world." He approached the blind man, interrupting his continual chanting. "May I offer you a plate of food? The roasted goat leg, yams, and vegetables are delicious. You must be hungry, for you sit by the eating house as a beggar would," he said cautiously, hoping to entice the man with food so that he might spare his life.

The man had been in the middle of telling yet another tale, something about a priest who had been murdered. "My stomach is well satisfied and I do not need to feed an appetite that does not exist," he said.

Toku'te's heart began to race once again, but he stood fast, keeping a calm expression on the outside. "I cannot afford to show this man that I am afraid, as much as each part of my body is urging me to flee as fast as I can," he thought. He was determined to convince the sorcerer not to disappear with him, and he was willing to put up a fight, even if the price was his life.

"I had a feeling I would meet you once again," the man said.

Toku'te thought in fear, "How can a blind man recognize a person he has never seen before? Worse, the light out here is so dim now, and even I can barely see my own feet." Then he addressed the man, "How do know of the world, when you do not have the ability to see?"

"How narrow-minded we humans often are," said the man with a laugh. "Sight is only one of many ways a person can see the world. From what you have just said, surely you can see for yourself that a blind man is able to see more than you, you who claims to have functioning eyes. It has been prophesized that the right person would be easy to recognize, no matter where he came from."

Toku'te's curiosity had been aroused. "Never have I seen or heard of a man like you, who seems to be a beggar, reject a delicious meal without a moment's hesitation and with such indifference as you have," he said in an effort to interrupt the man, who seemed to be about to launch into another tale, which would distract him.

Then, in order to satisfy his curiosity about whether the man was a sorcerer, Toku'te decided to ask. "Are you a sorcerer? Have you disguised yourself as a beggar in order to lure anyone who will listen to your deceitful, yet useful, tales to your strange land?"

The man laughed at the boy's naïveté, and then said, "What a very fortunate man I would be if I were a sorcerer." Hearing this, the boy immediately relaxed, but he still felt that maybe this was another trick the man was playing. However, the man's laughter made him feel somewhat embarrassed. He had always considered himself a courageous person, considering what he had been through, yet here was a stranger laughing at him because of a childish fear.

Toku'te said nothing and smiled, thinking the man could not see. Then he asked, "If you are neither a beggar nor a deceitful sorcerer, who are you and why are you acting in a way that a beggar or sorcerer would act?"

The man said nothing. He motioned the boy to sit on a flat rock that was close to where he sat. "It is not out of pleasure that a man willingly sits on the side of the road from sunrise to sunset telling tales that most people couldn't be bothered to listen to, but it is out of necessity," the man began. "A long time ago, ten years to be exact, I was the chief of a small village of about two thousand people. Because it was located in a great rain forest, the village was never threatened with a shortage of food, water, or land. It grew wealthier as the years passed, for by the blessing of the Gods the great trees of the forest offered us protection from even the largest army battalions." The man obviously had great pride in his village.

"Whether people live in the smallest village or the largest city, they all have beliefs that they live by and that determine how they live day by day." The man suddenly looked sad and ashamed. "Of these beliefs, we in my village believed that money was the root of all evil, and that those who were rich must be evil people, because they had become rich by evil means."

"But why have you come here to a strange land, assuming the manner of a filthy, hopeless beggar?" Toku'te interrupted, anxiously waiting for an explanation to the present situation.

"Costly it is indeed to assume the responsibility of a leader of many men and women," the man continued in a dejected tone with his head bowed. "I left my village not by choice, but because of humiliation. Some years ago, a man who had arrived from a far-off city situated in the desert came and stood before me. Because his city had been destroyed by an invading army, he pleaded that I grant him refuge in my village. His clothes were torn to shreds, he was badly injured, and he was thin from lack of food and water, as he had journeyed across the vast desert. Hoping that he might regain his dignity, I took pity on him and granted him refuge and employment as a leather craftsman, as that was his skill."

"But we in the village were shocked when we realized that after only five short years, the refugee had suddenly become very wealthy. He earned only a few coins crafting shields, sandals, water carriers, and many other leather goods. The craftsman of our village, for whom the refugee had been working, earned a lot more than he, and yet, after many years of labor, he had not seen such wealth, but here was a mere refugee, who might have been a runaway slave escaping the whip of his master, suddenly becoming a rich man."

"And this was only the beginning. The man seemed to grow wealthier with each passing month, and then one day he ordered an estate to be built, and he purchased about three hundred sheep and one hundred cattle. As chief of the village, I grew concerned about the possibility that he might be a man of great evil. No one could work at the same task as another and for a shorter duration and yet possess so much wealth. The belief that a man with much wealth must be evil seemed to be true, because that seemed to be the only explanation for the strange phenomenon."

"Early one morning, to my dismay, a woman and her husband came to my compound weeping with such unbearable intensity that I could not help but rise immediately to attend to their problem."

"My daughter … she is … she is gone!" cried the woman, who was down on her knees weeping uncontrollably. By then, many villagers who had heard the noise had gathered to observe the scene in pity. Some were shaking their heads, while some women tried to hold and calm the hopeless woman.

"According to the woman, her daughter had journeyed through the forest to visit her sick grandmother and was to return five days ago, according to the grandmother's messenger, who had arrived that day, five days since the departure of the daughter on her half-day journey back to the house of her mother. I thought perhaps the girl had been attacked and killed by a wild beast, or that she had been kidnapped by an evil person, which made me think instantly about the man to whom I had granted refuge. 'Maybe he was an evil man. Maybe he had come to ruin my village after he had had an unsuccessful attempt at a previous one,' I thought."

"The villagers seemed to have the same suspicions, for they urged me to question the man. None of the villagers had ever gone missing like this before, and if they had, they soon turned up, having lost their way and ending up in another village."

"So rather than send out a group of men to search for the girl, the man whom everyone suspected was questioned for the possibility that he had sold her as a slave to add to his wealth. Finally, at my command, the man was put to death in a most gruesome manner. He was hanged from a tree deep in the forest, where the beasts might feed on his evil flesh."

"But that same day, to my painful regret, a hunter from a nearby village had found the missing child and carried her home on his shoulders. He put her down, and she limped to her mother, who embraced her with joy."

"The hunter explained that the girl had stepped into a large trap hole and broken her leg and hit her head hard on the root of a tree. He had taken her home to his wife to care for her and had returned her home five days later. A shiver ran through my body at the realization of my mistake. I, a chief, had murdered a perfectly innocent and just man, all because of my ignorant beliefs."

"That night, sleep did not have the power to overcome my troubled mind. I was consumed with fearful thoughts of what might become of me and my village for such an unjust act. 'If I had but one more chance,' I thought. 'I would send out my men to each of the surrounding villages to look for the girl.' But instead, my foolish reliance on empty beliefs had brought me to my knees, where I was nothing but a regretful fool. The night grew older as I sank deeper into despair, trying to think about what I could do to right my wrong. But I was not to have such a chance."

"A deep and unfriendly voice called my name as I lay uncomfortably in my bed. The voice repeated my name, and I began to shiver. And then I saw the figure of the man who had been unjustly sentenced to a cruel death before his time."

Toku'te shivered as the old man related his tale. He had heard stories about men who had seen or communicated with ghosts, but until now he had always been skeptical.

"'Oh, you who call yourself a man among good and just men,' the old man continued as he related the story of his encounter with the ghost, 'You have betrayed your conscience. You have chosen instead to be led by your false judgment and intangible beliefs. Your belief that a man who has much wealth is evil because money is the root of all evil is a belief that is far from the real truth. The only truth that seems more appropriate is that the lack of wealth is the root of all evil,' thundered the ghost, showing no sign of mercy or forgiveness."

"'Tell me, Chief,' the ghost said to me. 'What can a poor man do who depends only on an income so small that his family must often skip their morning meal in order to have their afternoon meal, or skip that meal to have dinner? Would he not, because of the love for his family, do all that was necessary? Then in an effort to make ends meet, he becomes stressed and bitter because his long, exhausting days weigh heavily on him and he loses all joy in life and the world. And all this causes emotional and physical harm to his innocent family."

"'What is more evil than when a man flees from the responsibilities of his family in order to find freedom from such responsibilities? To my mind, nothing surpasses such evil against one's family. Yet it is with wealth that a man achieves a meaningful life. With wealth one could provide for one's family and have enough to live on without having to skip meals. A wealthy man could also make many sacrifices each month in honor of the Gods, or he could journey across vast lands in search of new wisdom and experience, until soon he too is able to teach his fellow men how they could become wealthy men, so that life would become more enjoyable, rather than be filled with bitterness from overwork and most of all, unhappiness. Thus, having money does not bring happiness; instead, it allows one to have access to the things that make a person happy.'"

"The ghost stopped and pointed straight at me with a shaky finger and an angry face, and my fear for the worst instantly became a reality when he said, 'Chief, you were a good man. You granted me permission to settle in your village, but then, with my sentencing to an unjust death, you took from me the opportunity to teach my fellow men how to become wealthy, and for that, you and your village shall pay the price. I hereby curse you to forever wander the face of the earth, going from village to village, city to city, reciting life's lessons with eyes that are as useless as the lifeless body of the man you have made me!' The ghost's voice rose so loud that it sounded like thunder."

"Early in the morning I rose, hoping that the terrifying event had just been a dream, but then I realized that my eyes would not open, and reality quickly settled in. Realizing what humiliation I would be subjected to by the villagers if they found out that their chief was nothing but a blind fool, I quickly fled the village."

"'It is unfortunate indeed when the chief himself is subjected to such humiliation,' said a woman who sounded as though she was quite elderly. She had taken me into her home after she had found me with her sheep in their pen, nearly unconscious."

"I had suffered much hardship after I left my village. The world is not kind to those who are less fortunate," the blind man said in self-pity. "An animal enjoys a far better life. I had been robbed many times of my few possessions and afterward badly beaten."

"But surely there is no suffering that lasts a lifetime," the blind man said, now in a more cheerful tone. Toku'te continued to sit in silence, speaking not so much as a word, he was so absorbed in the blind man's story.

The man adjusted his position and continued, "I had come to that morning on the floor of a small hut to the pain of my wounds as the woman cleaned them. 'You are lucky you were not killed,' she said."

"'Lucky!' I exclaimed. 'A man who cannot see is nothing but unlucky. I must go through life, day by day, always easy prey to the many misfortunes that love only to torment men of lesser ability.' I told the woman about what had brought me my misfortune. She said nothing, but grabbed my hand and examined it."

"'You are indeed a good man, but the wind of misfortune has made you its victim, blowing you into a deep, dark hole that only you can find your way out of,' she said. 'Yet the wind of luck does favor you, for it has blown you into my path. If you would trust me, young man, I will show you the way that will allow you to see with your eyes once again.'"

"Skeptically, I said, 'That would be impossible, for there is nothing any mortal could do to overcome the curse of an angry ghost whose life has been taken unjustly.' The woman ran her hand smoothly from the top of my head and down over my face."

"'A word like impossible can only limit the greatness of man, for things are as you see them, be they possible or impossible. I am a daughter of a great fortune-teller, and from him I have learned how to read and understand one's palm and direct a person on the best course of action to take. But this will work only if you want me to help you.'"

"My misery and frustration from and wandering hopelessly was too great a burden to bear. Having no other choice, without hesitation I decided to take a chance; after all, I really had nothing to lose."

"'It is not for your sake that I shall help you, but for the sake of the people of your village, whom you have ruled for many years,' the woman continued after I had given her my consent."

"'After losing its chief, your village has fallen into chaos. The weak are pitted against the strong, different groups are fighting for power, and because no one plays their traditional role any longer, the village is slowly becoming uninhabitable. In as little as five years, if the village does not witness your return, the villagers will flee to nearby cities or villages in search of a better life. As for you, the severity of the misfortune you face right now is minor compared with the misfortune that you will surely suffer if you fail to return to your people in time.'"

"'What must I do to avoid such misfortune?' I cried out helplessly."

"'You must help him!' the woman replied."

"'Who?'"

"'He who has shown much courage, despite his great fear, in realizing his desire, which was shown to him in a dream,' she replied calmly. 'This is a young man who pursued his dream despite the will of his traditions, and because of this he will forever be haunted by the anger and resentment of a bitter heart!'"

"I continued to journey from one city to the next, preaching aloud the lessons of life, for the woman had told me that the man I must help will be the one who stands a while in my presence as I tell these lessons, for he is one with much curiosity." Toku'te's heart began to beat faster, only this time, he was afraid of suffering the misfortune of endless bitterness.

"It is I the woman had spoken of. I am the one who left the house of my father against his will and tradition to pursue the dream that my heart had shown me. I beg you, tell me what I must do to avoid such a fate, so that it not too late for either of us. I am nothing but an innocent dreamer, struggling to win a battle against tradition, with the odds so unjustly arranged in favor of those who care not about innovation and change, who want only the same thing from sunup to sundown, day after day, from one generation to the next. I am determined to win this battle, and I shall do all that is necessary to do so," Toku'te pleaded with the blind man. Though he had grown much older since the time he had left the house of his father, he could still feel inside him that young boy with the same burning desire and faith to make the so-called impossible possible.

"Son," the blind man began, "Your father is a good man—even more than you have ever given him credit for. He lies very ill in his house with his aging heart full of despair for his only son. Because you, a great farmer, chose a path other than that ordered by tradition, he is angry at himself for his failure as a father. He fears the fate that may descend on you for your treason, for never have ancestors forgiven the man who turns his back on tradition as you have."

"If he dies feeling this way, you will be cursed for all eternity with so much despair and regret that you will despise your own success, and like many unfortunate men, you will be sad for the rest of your breathing days."

"You must appear before your father and plead with him for his good will; this is the only way you will have a chance to escape from such unhappiness."

Toku'te was shaken by what he had heard, and he felt a chill run down his spine. Despite this, however, he chose to remain calm, as something inside gave him a feeling of comfort. It said, "Just believe that everything will be okay, and so it shall be. You made it this far all alone, what more are you afraid of?"

He thanked the blind man for his guidance and wished him well. The blind man had told him leave for the house of his father the next day, for a heart of an old man filled with so much pain could last only a short while before giving up the fight.

That night, Toku'te's eyes would not close in sleep, as much as he tried; thoughts of the day's events occupied his mind. "It is indeed very true that nothing occurs without a purpose. Everything happens for a reason," he thought as he recalled the chief's story. "Had he not ordered the killing of the wealthy man, he would not have come here to warn me of the great misfortune that only the Gods could have foreseen."

"Every misfortune comes with a seed of equivalent fortune," he thought, remembering what his mother had once said to him when he had badly injured himself with the hoe as he worked the farm.

"The ghost really intended to help the chief rather than curse him for all his life, for now the chief will now be able to return to his village and lead his people to much prosperity, for the lessons of life really were lessons he himself needed to learn."

Toku'te had acquired a camel for his journey home and loaded it with gifts for his parents and food and water for his trip. It was a quiet, foggy morning, a bit colder than usual, but he didn't mind; the heat of the afternoon was so great that this was a blessing.

As a courtesy, he decided to look for the blind man to say goodbye before he departed. After all, it was because of him that the man had endured such hardship.

"Toku'te!" a voice called out from behind him. He had been heading toward the eating house where he had found the man the night before. He steered his camel around with his customary curiosity to see who was calling.

"Chief! You can see!" Toku'te sang out with joy and excitement, seeing the blind man sitting on a horse with his once-closed eyes wide open.

The chief responded with the same enthusiasm, saying, "Come, I shall treat you to a last meal before you make your departure on the long road to the house of your father. It is a custom in my village to show gratitude for another's goodwill, and to honor this, I offer you a meal."

Toku'te accepted willingly and followed the man into the eating house.

Only a short time had passed when the two men finished their heavy breakfast, after which a series of short and long burps began forcing their way out of the two men's stomachs.

The sun had just made its appearance over the horizon as rows of donkeys, camels, and horses entered the marketplace; it was as though the Gods had just brought the place alive with a single finger snap.

"You ought to be grateful for your age and good fortune," the chief began after taking a sip from his cup of thick, hot cassava drink, which was well sweetened with honey. "Only a few men are fortunate enough to actually follow their dream, many of which come to them as recurring dreams, pulling on their soul, seeking attention. You have also done this at the right age, not, as many people do, just before they enter the gates of old age, after time has been wasted and it is too late and their only motivation is regret. I envy your good fortune, and yet I am satisfied to have found you."

The chief smiled contentedly, and then he said, "Before you go, I will share with you one last lesson of life. During my days of hardship due to my blindness, I came to a city that was said to be the home of a very wise and powerful man—so wise that wealthy fathers from far-off lands sent their children to learn wisdom from him."

"A blunt yet kind man, he fed me and provided me with an escort party so that I could go through the thick forest without getting lost or killed by the hungry beasts of the forest when I left his home."

"For your benefit and those you meet, and to ensure your success, I will share with you the wisdom the wise man shared with me and a group of young men who once sat before him."

"The wise man said that there were six rules that can make or break a person. According to him, people who respect the wisdom of these six rules and make them a part of their life will be successful, whereas those who do not will be doomed to the random winds of life, which will blow them to an undesirable end."

"A man must strive to be definite in his endeavors; in other words, he must have a vision. This is vital if any man truly desires to make his dream a reality, for a vision is like the stars that shine brightly and reliably in the night sky, and on which a caravan leader crossing the vast desert can rely on to lead him, his followers and their prized possessions safely out of the hot, dry, inhospitable land."

"If one does not have a definite purpose, or vision, for their life, he will become an unfortunate victim, and if he were the caravan leader, for instance, he would be a sorry fellow. He and his followers would be doomed to die of hunger and thirst because they would veer off from their intended course, wandering deeper into the heart of the desert, where they would be forced into painful submission and eventually death at the hands of the desert, or robbers, who know well how to navigate the desert."

"Thus, if one does not know his destination, then, without fail, one will surely be chosen for him, be it good or bad. Son, you have followed the first of the rules to make your dream a reality," the chief said, looking at Toku'te. "You have discovered your own definite purpose—your desire to become a wealthy merchant."

Toku'te said nothing; he only nodded his head in agreement, eagerly waiting to hear what the other rules were.

"The second rule that makes a man successful in his life is the nature of the thoughts he adopts as his own.

According to the wise man, this is a rule that all men take for granted and are often too carefree about; yet it is the rule that shapes their lives moment by moment, day by day, month by month, year by year, and, eventually, throughout their lifetime!"

The chief turned to Toku'te and asked, "What is the difference between a beggar who sits helplessly on the side of the road in front of an eating house, hoping for the warm leftovers of the departing customers, and a man who rides on a beautifully designed chariot made with a rare wood and an abundance of gold and drawn by two handsome white horses that are as swift as the wind and driven by a well-dressed man who takes his master wherever he wishes to go?"

"One is wealthy and happy the other is poor and miserable," Toku'te responded quickly.

"It is as you say," said the chief. "But that is not all of it. The main difference is this: It is the way that each man has permitted himself to think!"

"Consider this," he said, leaning towards his listener, who was now puzzled. "Each and every one of us started out without any substantial possessions, except if one were favored by the Gods and born into a wealthy family, but even then he would still have nothing, as he would not yet have inherited his family's wealth."

"It is we who choose the kind of life we will live. Let's return to the beggar and the wealthy man. In all likelihood the wealthy man would have focused most of his thoughts on prosperity and having and keeping wealth, and slowly, over time, the reality of these thoughts would become attracted to him, whereas the poor beggar would have spent his time consumed by negative thoughts of misery and poverty."

"A wealthy man would think thoughts such as, 'I am a very wealthy, wise, and able man,' or, 'I feel deep gratitude toward the Gods for blessing me with the vast estate on which I live in comfort with my family,' even though he may live in only a small, cramped, hot, and humid hut and earn very little income."

"On the other hand, the beggar would think thoughts such as, 'How unfortunate I am to live a life of such poverty,' or, 'Nothing I could do would change my situation, for I am nothing but a man of no abilities,' or, 'This must be a punishment from the Gods, for I am nothing but a poor and miserable fellow.'"

Toku'te was confused, and he said, "What you say seems to be true, but I still do not understand how a man's thoughts can become his reality. Are not a man's thoughts separate from the world about him?" He then pointed to the marketplace and asked, "Could a man not go to the marketplace, buy a cow, and start a herd? What have thoughts got to do with his ability to take action?" Toku'te looked at the chief, waiting for an answer.

"Yes, one can indeed go to the marketplace and buy a cow and build a herd, and no one can deny such an occurrence; however, a man's thoughts influence his actions, his actions influence the results, and then, ultimately, the results will determine the type of life he lives. Look at this series of events in another light: The man's thoughts always, without fail, equal his reality. So if one desires to change his life, he must first change his thoughts."

Toku'te nodded his head slowly as he began to make sense of what he had heard. "Having a definite purpose, as you said earlier, is a guide in the sense that if the nature of one's thoughts were as if his definite purpose were a reality, the thoughts would bring him to what he greatly desires." The chief was so impressed with his student that he took the opportunity to praise him.

"The third of these six qualities is *discipline*: one's ability to do what needs to be done when it needs to be done. The failure to follow this rule is one reason why people fail to achieve their goals, even if they have vision and control over their thoughts."

Toku'te was surprised at how closely the rules were interrelated.

"The accomplishment of any definite purpose does not come without paying a heavy price—a price that is paid daily and always in advance. The price is hard work and determination. We humans are lazy by nature; many of us will not easily rise before the sun or continue to work into the evening after the sun has set, but to realize a dream, we must work long hours. In other words, it is by extraordinary effort alone that we can make it. It is this and only this that separates successful men from men who are content with what life throws at them."

"Tell me," said the chief, "What can one achieve if he works for only a fraction of the day?"

"Hardly anything," Toku'te replied.

"That's true," the chief acknowledged, nodding his head. "And any work done poorly results only in failure. The only reliable source of discipline one can depend on is the vision of one's definite purpose. When one knows exactly what it is he desires and has a mental picture of what it would look like if it were a reality, only then will he develop the determination to work from morning till night every day, persisting in good or bad times until finally he makes it to his destination, and then he embarks on an even greater journey. Those who are left behind look at those who are successful with envy. They are the unfortunate ones who gave up when the going got tough, choosing to blame their so-called lack of good luck for their failure, rather than themselves for choosing to fail by deciding to give up."

The waiter brought the two conversing patrons two cups filled to the top with cold water. Because the eating house would not be busy for a while, the waiter did not trouble the customers for occupying their seats for a longer time.

"The fourth rule that is essential to making a successful life is to *manage one's fears*," the chief continued after taking a sip of the cold water and clearing his throat. "Fear is the greatest and most powerful force in the world against all men, yet it is also the most intangible. Fear exists only in our mind, and it has a power so great that it could stop a man dead in his tracks if he gives it the opportunity to express itself!"

"The wise man spoke of two types of fear. The first is the *fear of failure*, which robs the unfortunate men who fall victim to its trap of a lifetime of worthwhile achievements. Fear of failure makes a dream impossible to achieve, thus the fear of failure is greater than failure itself. A man who fears that he may fail will not engage in the enterprise of his dreams, or travel to places he would like to see, or learn to play a lyre."

"Ah!" the chief boomed. "We must not fear failure, because success is impossible without the pain we experience and lessons we learn from failure—whether small or great. Is it not by failing at a task many times over that we become good at that task? Does the apprentice to a chariot maker build his first chariot as good in quality as that of his master? No! It is sad that only a few people realize that with time, the pain of failure only transforms into the many joys of success!"

"The second type of fear is the *fear of criticism*. With this fear, we are afraid of the criticism that would follow if we were to fail. The most common source of this criticism is from our family and close companions. It is not because they dislike our area of interest, but because they have much love for us, and because of this they do not want us to come to any harm, and they would do anything in their power to protect us."

"The criticism that we experience over our failures can result in road blocks, stopping us each time another opportunity makes its brief appearance. The fear of criticism that may result if we fail can become of greater importance to us than the successful accomplishment of what we want to do, which would have led to much joy and prosperity. However, the critics are mere humans just like everyone else, with their own fears to deal with; therefore, it makes sense for us to live our life free of the boundaries set by our fear of what others might say."

"*Willingness to learn* is the fifth rule that makes a successful person. It is the foundation for all the other rules. Knowledge is power when applied with persistent discipline."

"According to the wise man, a person who is knowledgeable in the affairs of war has the ability to destroy, with little effort, an army twice the size of his if the army depended on nothing but manpower."

"There are abundant sources of knowledge for any area that you would choose to learn about, be it baking, bricklaying, farming, merchandising, chariot making, or shepherding. The only requirement for this is to seek out people with the desired knowledge, and once found, you will realize that generous is the tongue of lifelong experience, for it loves to wag. Knowledgeable people with experience will gladly share with the interested student. Therefore, all people must strive to be at the forefront of progress, seizing without hesitation the opportunity to learn from others wiser than they, lest they rot like the overripe fruit of yesterday."

"It is all making sense now," Toku'te thought, recalling his experiences from the night he first had the strange dream, to his master's diary, where he learned how to use his money, to the day he had the courage to turn his back on tradition, and all the other strange people and experiences he had encountered up to that moment.

"What a different story I would tell if I had chosen instead to reject my dream and remain content to be a simple man, farming for a living. I have experienced all that the wise man told the chief without even realizing it," Toku'te thought in surprise.

"Of the six rules that make a man's life a success, the last rule is of the greatest importance, for if it is followed it will be the most likely to allow us to achieve peace and happiness. This rule is that we must *handle money profitably*."

Before the chief could utter another word, Toku'te said enthusiastically, "But Chief, I already know all about that. I have a whole book that was given to me by a very wealthy man, and it is because of it that I have been able to accumulate the small wealth that I have now from my enterprise!"

The chief smiled and said nothing for a short while, and then he placed his hand on Toku'te's shoulder and said, "You, my friend, are one of few wise young men I have ever met in my travels; I have no doubt in your knowledge and ability. I am not telling you all that I have learned because of your lack of knowledge or ignorance; by God, no! I am telling you to remind you of what you already know and to bring to light what you do not yet know."

Toku'te was embarrassed; he regretted having said what he did, but the man was indifferent, for he thought only, "The spirit of youth never fails to make its appearance, even in old age, when people think they know all there is to know about a subject."

The chief continued, "Son, my advice to you is this: It is best to make good use of your ears rather than your mouth; the former brings great rewards and satisfaction, while the latter brings misery and dissatisfaction, stealing from you the opportunity to benefit from new knowledge." Toku'te humbly held back his desire to speak, choosing instead to listen to the man's words of wisdom.

The chief continued to relate the wisdom of the wise man until the sun was high in the sky, and the eating house began to fill with the people from the marketplace, looking to satisfy their midday appetite.

Toku'te and the chief left the eating house and climbed onto their respective animals. "May the Gods see you through to your chosen destination," the chief said, smiling as he motioned his horse with a crack of his whip in the direction of his village. "Courage … determination …" Toku'te could barely hear these final words as the man disappeared behind a thick cloud of dust that rose behind his galloping horse.

Before departing, Toku'te had arranged with the son of his master to look after his enterprise while he was away. He was a trustworthy man and was skilled in the ways of good merchants. In return for his service, Toku'te had agreed to share his profit with him.

Wise men have a saying: "The end of a person's exploration is when he arrives at the place where he first began—when he gets to know that place for the first time."

Toku'te traveled along the same familiar path he had taken when he first left the house of his father. He looked with a great satisfaction at the goods and the sizeable bag of gold that clunked with the side-to-side rocking of the saddlebag. He remembered when he was a boy, far from manhood, being forced to set out on his own without a single coin to his name, except for his bag of savings and an empty stomach growling for attention and a hot plate of food.

"I am grateful to you, oh great Gods, for inspiring me with the courage to walk with faith the path of greatest resistance, a path that was so dark and painful. Such feelings of joy would be strange to me had I not taken my dream as seriously as I did," he thought to himself, closing his eyes in short meditation as he flowed with the rhythm of the camel.

As he came to his village, many children surrounded the camel, shouting in excitement at the sight of the animal. Toku'te gently greeted with a smile those children who bothered to pay any attention to him; most of them were enthralled by the camel, and Toku'te knew the camel would not hurt them, as it had a gentle nature. Toku'te could not help but notice the increased number of children in his village, and also the surrounding farmland seemed a little barren compared with the way it had been, but apart from this, everything else seemed to have remained the same.

Camels were a rare sight in his village because traveling merchants only went to the marketplace in the city to sell their goods. A journey to the village would not be worth the effort, for the poor farmers don't have much to offer in exchange for the merchants' expensive goods.

A short time later, the familiar gate to the compound of Toku'te's father's home came into view. Suddenly his heart leapt.

The family compound held many memories for Toku'te, both bitter and pleasant. Yet regardless of what had happened, it was time to set things right, he thought as he dismounted from his camel.

"Oh, my son, so long gone, you have returned to your beloved mother!" Toku'te's mother cried, tears filling her eyes, as she threw her arms around her son. Her face was now deeply wrinkled, and her hair, once black, had turned completely white.

"Old age is inescapable by no one, not even my own mother," he thought as he held his mother in a soft embrace.

Kissing his forehead, his mother looked up to the sky and said, "Surely you Gods are kind, for you have answered the prayer of a much-burdened soul longing for the safe return of her son in good health.

I thank you for this." Then she said, looking into his eyes, "Tell me, my son, have you achieved your dream?"

"Not all of it yet," he replied. "I have come to understand much about wealth and I have prospered, but I also realize that without happiness in one's heart, riches are useless."

"You have grown into a wise young man. I had much faith in your ability to make your dream a reality."

Toku'te sat in the compound with his mother, telling her all about his years of travel and adventure, while he waited for his father to awaken from his deep slumber. His mother laughed and cried as he told his story, saying at the end how fortunate she was to have a son with a strong and determined spirit.

The evening crept in slowly as the two reconnected, getting caught up on everything that had happened over the long years they had been separated. Toku'te particularly wanted to know what had happened the day he had left the house.

Joyful at the arrival of her long-gone son, his mother hesitated to bring up the pains of the past, but Toku'te urged her to tell him, and she finally decided to speak of it.

"Your father was greatly angered by your choice to turn your back on your tradition. His rage continued for many days, so that even I became a victim of it. 'It is because of you that he left to follow a hopeless dream that is nothing but a sure path to disaster. Have you neither shame nor pity for your son's life?' he would say to me. 'The world out there is no place for the mere son of a farmer, who no longer chooses this occupation! Besides, you should appreciate the blessings of the Gods, who with their generosity blessed you with a son, or have you forgotten the pain and hardship you experienced to bring him into this world?' My heart cried helplessly as he delivered each stinging insult; after all, what does a man know about being a mother?"

"Yet the courage and conviction that I saw in your eyes was enough to give me faith that you would accomplish what you so desired. This kept the tears away most of the time during your absence." The woman took the loose end of her worn-out garment and wiped her eyes.

"Even greater was my faith in your success and safety when Agilo, our good neighbor, had returned from a buying expedition for the good king with a message and the pieces of gold that you had sent. Thank you, my son, for your generosity."

"Son, your father loves you very much, it is only the unfavorable circumstances that brought out the worst in him …" She was then interrupted by a familiar sound that always indicated that Toku'te's father was near—the loud clearing of his throat.

His father had emerged from the hut in which he had lain for many months, unable to assume his usual hardworking nature. He had become a victim of ill health.

Toku'te immediately fell to his knees, greeting him in their traditional way. He was shocked at the sight of his father and stayed on his knees, staring at the ground with his heart racing. The experience seemed to be even worse than when he first encountered the blind man at the market square.

"Will my father ever forgive me for such treason against the tradition of my forefathers? Or will he once again banish me forever, never to return to this house again, dooming me to become an unhappy wealthy merchant? My mother would have no will to live if her only son were to leave her forever." Thoughts such as these were running through Toku'te's mind when his father interrupted, saying, as he gently laid his hand on his son's head, "It is as your mother has said, I love you very much, and it is my duty as your father to protect you from harm. It is indeed true that circumstances often bring out the worst in people of any character, for they can lose the ability to reason properly in such situations." Toku'te's father sat down beside his wife and son. "You are my only son, and you are the only one in the family to carry on the legacy of your forefathers. I could not bear to think of the possibility that you might become a failure, here in the village or in any city."

"Farming, as my father and his father and so on have done was the safest way for each of them to make of himself a man of means, able to feed his family. It is because I love you that I rejected the merchant's path, or any other similar path, for you, for the merchant's world is filled with the possibility of failure and unhappiness that could allow you no chance of earning enough to reliably take care of a family. It requires the utmost careful planning to be prepared to keep a family well." Toku'te didn't bother to say anything; he only sat there relieved, yet greatly surprised at such a radical change in his father's character.

"'What does the son of a farmer know about making himself a rich merchant?' I asked myself," his father continued. 'At farming he would survive, but in such an unknown world as merchandising, he would perish.'

"I too at a young age had learned to be a skilled farmer from my father, who had been well taught by his father. He taught me how to grow and reap the most profitable harvest, so that I could earn coins to sacrifice to the Gods as well as provide for a family of my own. One day the Gods sent me a dream that I should become a dealer in leather, serving those who lived in the city and those who traveled from other lands. I was very excited, for the dream appeared to me to be a message from the Gods, and my father had always told me that dreams are the way that the Gods talked to us. When I told my father about my dream, he said, 'It must be a curse. The Gods test men for their willingness to follow the tradition of their forefathers, and if they fail the test, the consequences will be painful.' Despite this warning, I decided to act behind his back."

"I began to save every spare coin I had, hoping to save enough to buy leather from the merchants who brought it to the city from distant lands."

"After many months of saving I did just that. I first looked around the marketplace for the merchant with the best quality leather that I could afford to buy. With luck, or at least so I thought, I stumbled upon a middle-aged man who claimed to be from the city where the best leather was cured and sold in large quantities. His leather was of such fine quality that the king himself bought from him for all the city's needs, such as for making the army's uniforms. In my youth and inexperience, I was filled with joy for having found just the right merchant. After all, the king was his customer; I would be a mad fool to pass up such an opportunity, and besides, I was eager to prove that my father's interpretation of my dream was wrong. But as the unfortunate events began to unfold, I quickly realized that my father was correct. After the merchant insisted that I prove that I had the money to buy the leather, he requested that I follow him to see his stock, which was in storage at the large storage shed at the edge of the market …"

No longer able to speak, Toku'te's father shook his bowed head, and with great disappointment in his voice he continued, "The man led me into a small shed that stank of horse manure. There, two men had been lying in hiding; the merchant signaled to them by slamming the door shut with a loud bang. Immediately I was thrown on the ground. One man took my small pouch of savings, while the merchant and the other man beat me badly till I was almost unconscious. One of them said as he laughed and kicked me repeatedly in the stomach, 'That will surely teach you the painful lesson to never trust a stranger!' The three men fled, while I lay on the ground badly injured and bleeding from my wounds. I later found out from the king's crier, who paraded up and down the marketplace delivering the king's messages, that these men were known to work together to rob any victim who was unprotected, and that even the king's chancellor had become a victim of this notorious group of thieves."

"'That really was a test by the Gods,' I thought to myself as I struggled to find my way home. And when I told my father what had happened, he said, 'I am glad that you now believe that tradition is the only path.' I was devastated. 'The Gods must be as cruel as they are kind to play such callous joke on a man! Could they not have found a less painful way to test one?' I thought angrily."

"Yet in spite of my anger and frustration, I made a vow to myself that I would become a skilled farmer and work very hard at it, and that if my son had such a dream, I would not let him go through such pain by going against the word of his father."

"Son, I may have been angry with you for your choice for many days after you had been gone, and I disowned you as my son, but I was only making the utmost effort to protect you from such an end, for the world today is no safer than when I was a young man. A careless and inexperienced young man such as you could be killed if robbers like those ones got hold of you. If I had allowed you to do what you wished to do, I would have broken the oath that I had taken and been doomed to the life of an unfortunate man who failed to raise his son properly, as I was raised by my own father, and as he was raised by his father. Every breathing moment would be a nightmare, for there can be no peace or happiness for a man so doomed."

"If I had but one more chance," Toku'te's father said slowly, with tears rolling down his cheeks, "I would have been the one to go through the hardships that you have gone through, and by now I would have become a very wealthy merchant with a great estate and much gold for your inheritance."

"In all the many years I have lived as an adult, never have I ever seen a child teach his parents a lesson that even they could not have learned by themselves. You have taught this old fool a lesson of a lifetime, my son, and that lesson is this: Traditions can also change. It is as though the Gods gave you the power and courage to leave your father's house as you did to ensure that you and your family's future would be secure. It is obvious to the naked eye that the farmland here is beginning to turn into desert sand and can no longer hold water or seeds. As a result, our harvest has become poorer with each year, and the merchants and buyers have shunned us in favor of the harvest of other areas with more fertile farmland. Because you used your eyes not only for sight, but also for vision, you did not turn your back on your dream of becoming a rich merchant with much means, and so you are not a sorry victim who is heir to an obsolete tradition."

Toku'te's mother, smiling as she observed the two men now at peace, said, "It is as the Gods willed it that everything that happens does not happen without a purpose. I am only thankful that there is once again peace in this house as there once was, for nothing brings more joy than the laughter of one's family, who, because of differing opinions, had raised a barrier of ill feeling towards one another."

Toku'te sat silent with a smile on his face as he watched his father embrace his wife. He thought about how everything did happen for a reason. "What would have happened to the chief if he had not mustered up all that courage to turn his back on his tradition? Would he be doomed to walk the rest of his breathing days blind, unable to return to his village, which was on the brink of destruction?"

That night, Toku'te lay his head down to sleep, but he could not; the events that had happened over the past many years filled his mind. He finally realized that a dream is just a dream. "It was like giving a man the option of either pushing a door open or leaving it closed, and it was a choice that had to be made," he thought as he reflected on the night he had awakened after he had dreamed of being a wealthy merchant. Now he was well on the way to realizing his dream, which had seemed to be an impossible achievement for a mere farmer's son who knew nothing of the ways of a merchant.

"Regret must be a very painful burden to bear," Toku'te thought as he recalled his father's story. "It is impossible for him to return to the past to take the opportunities that he had once neglected to pursue. Maybe it was my father whom the Gods intended to task with the duty of saving the blind chief from his misery, but when he failed to persevere in the face of the forces of tradition, the Gods decided to shift the task to me. Come to think about it, one's ability to be tenacious despite the obstacles he faces is the difference between a joyful soul and a soul burdened with regret," he thought, reflecting on his wandering in pursuit of his dream, for it was his unwillingness to quit that won him employment at the stable of the horse trader, and that gave him the courage to speak of his dream to his father against the will of tradition, thus making him a happy man for having faith in his dream and helping him avoid the unhappiness caused by regret.

"Son, the Gods may test your faith in the tradition of your ancestors by sending you misleading dreams," his father had told him once when he was only a few years old. "You must be cautious and avoid misfortune."

"If my father had been right in saying this, then it is a fair conclusion to say that even the Gods make mistakes!"

"It is often those who have the courage and tenacity to pursue a dream that seems impossible that makes the greatest difference of all," a choir of men sang out during the festival of the harvest at the marketplace.

Many years had come and gone since Toku'te, against the will of his traditional father, had chosen the path shown to him in a dream. The city is now as prosperous as any king would desire his city to be, for it was Toku'te's students, who, after learning the profitable handling of their wages, had grown more prosperous. What were once a row of red mud huts had now been replaced by houses made of stone, each of a design unique to its owner's desire.

The streets were bustling not only with the activity of the farmers, who came in from the country to sell their produce, and laborers going about their business throughout the day, but also with men riding in beautiful chariots led by healthy, well-fed horses, carrying them to wherever they wished to go. Over time, the city had grown so prosperous that merchants from the far reaches of the earth came to trade their goods. It had also become a trusted destination for many youth, who were sent by their fathers to learn the valuable wisdom needed to live a worthy existence.

It is only by inspiration that any man, regardless of what life has dealt him, may make himself a valued and respected man in his community, even if he had been a beggar for most of his life, or if he is overwhelmed by the burdens of debt. It is for the latter that Toku'te had spent the rest of his life teaching and inspiring his fellow citizens so that they too could, by themselves, develop in their soul the will to effect positive change in their life, and hence be empowered to pursue their dreams, while greatly increasing their chances of becoming happier and prosperous citizens.

The arrival terminal at the airport was crowded with people, some rushing up and down the vast hallways, others sitting in small groups on the rows of black seats, while others stood anxiously at the arrival gates, peering over the heads of other people to try to catch a glimpse from a distance of their loved ones.

In this latter group was Tunde, the man who had once been a beggar on the streets of New York City. Only four years had passed since he had returned to find the soggy brown envelope that had suddenly disrupted his comfortable life as a beggar. Now he was waiting for the arrival of his family.

"How crazy and eventful those years were," he thought, looking up the ceiling in gratitude to God. "It is as though a blanket of dark clouds had suddenly been replaced by a clear blue sunny sky. My late mother was right; patience is a great virtue. After all, I have finally made myself a man among men after years of never-ending pain and suffering, all thanks to a kind young lady who gave me the gift of a book that guided me along."

Suddenly a set of arms appeared out of nowhere and embraced the man in a tight hug. It was his wife, a young woman who had lived as if she were a widow, waiting far too long for her husband. The burden of prolonged loneliness was finally cured in an instant by repeated kisses and hugs.

"Sweetheart, forgive me for taking …" his wife interrupted him with another kiss on his lips, indicating that everything was okay, and gave him a light punch to his stomach, which made them both laugh.

Tunde kissed his little boy saying, "I missed you! Look at you, you're such a big boy," and then he sat the boy on his shoulders and they headed for the parking lot.

Learn what happens to the unfortunate beggar,
Tunde, in the second of Yahaya Baruwa's trilogy,
Tunde: A Man of Lost Ambition

Read 25 pages from
Tunde: A Man of Lost Ambition for FREE!

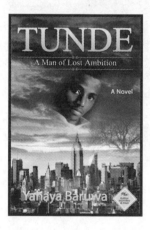

Download your FREE pages right now at www.My-Tunde.com

If you enjoy these pages, and you are sure to do so,
you can then purchase the complete book.

This is my gift to you.
Thank You for reading my books!
Yahaya Baruwa

Claim Your <u>Free</u> T-shirt!

Get one of four fan T-shirts absolutely <u>FREE</u> when you buy <u>2-gift copies</u> of *Struggles of a Dreamer*.

The Perfect Gift for:

- Graduation   - Birthdays
- Weddings   - Your Book Club
- Anniversaries - Travel
- Housewarming
- or for the Bookworm in your life who just can't have enough books!

Available in:

-Black

-White

-Blue

-Red

*T-shirt style and design may vary

$~~~~~$ ~~59.95~~

Only...
<u>$39.95!</u>

<u>ORDER NOW!</u>
<u>*Call*</u>: 647.628.9250 or

<u>*Email*</u>: *ybaruwa@yahaya.ca*

Order within the next <u>24 hours</u> and Receive <u>Free</u> Shipping!*

*Free shipping in Ontario only

Methods of Payment: Credit Card via *Paypal; Interac Email Transfer*; Cheque or Cash